MECHANICAL
ABERDEEN

MECHANICAL ABERDEEN

An Engineering View of Aberdeen's Industries
from 1888 - 1913, the First 25 Years of the
Aberdeen Mechanical Society.

John S. Reid

To Aenea, Iain and Hamish

Typeset in 10pt Times Roman and printed on 135gsm High Speed Opal, natural tint
by Halcon Printing Ltd., Units 5 & 6, Spurryhillock Industrial Estate, Stonehaven AB3 2NH

First Published by Keith Murray Publishing/JSR, December 1990.
46 Portal Crescent, Tillydrone, Aberdeen AB2 2SP.

ISBN 1 870978 31 5

Contents

Preface

Anyone who has tried to find out about Aberdeen's traditional industries in some detail will have faced difficulties. Facts are scattered and photographs almost as rare as hens' teeth. Postcards, the commercial motivation for many city photographs now of historic value, were rarely made of industrial scenes. Long-lived local firms have not kept systematic photographic archives nor, in most cases, even a digested record of their own development. In consequence, it was with some hesitation that I accepted an offer to talk to the Aberdeen Mechanical Society in 1988 about their foundation one hundred years before, and about the context of industrial Aberdeen at that time. As it turned out, my reluctance was soon dispelled upon seeing the Minute Books of the Society. These recorded the talks presented at Society meetings and, in particular, the programme of visits to local and more distant industry undertaken by the Society. My own brief talk was sustained by those Minute Books and their continued interest has led to the publication of this account. I am most grateful to the Centenary Committee of the Society for their invitation and in particular to the Joint Secretary of the Aberdeen Mechanical Society, Henry Barber, for supporting my interest and making the Minute Books available for an extended period.

It would be wrong to suggest that all the information in the following pages comes directly from the Aberdeen Mechanical Society, for a great deal has been found elsewhere. For the photographs I am extremely grateful to the following firms who have been kind enough to allow their archival material to appear in these pages: Aberdeen Journals Ltd. (Tom Forsythe), ACW Ltd. (David Stewart), J. & J. Crombie Ltd. (Isobel Smith), Northern Co-operative Society Ltd. (James Mutch), Richards p.l.c. (Ian Thomson), Thomas Tait & Sons Ltd. (Sheila Tait) and John M. Henderson & Co. Ltd. (Alan Grattidge). My thanks also go to Bert Rendell of Grampian Region Water Services who lent some of the excellent pictures in chapter 6, to the Aberdeen Harbour Board (John Turner) for material in chapter 4, to the North East of Scotland Museum Services (David Bertie), to Mike Dey and John Edwards of Aberdeen Art Gallery & Museums for material in several chapters, and to John Lovie for archival gasworks photographs in chapter 3. To Gibby Shepherd I am particularly grateful for the care he has taken in reproducing original prints and pictures, many of which were showing their age. On behalf of my readers, I should like to thank Murray Hadden and Lynn Forbes of Halcon Printing Ltd., for the trouble they have taken in laying out the work and reproducing the pictures. Any remaining blemishes in the prints reflect the antiquity of the originals and not defects of reproduction.

For illustrative material and helpful advice I am pleased to acknowledge the contribution of our local libraries. These include Aberdeen City Libraries Local Section, the Aberdeen University Library Archives (Colin McLaren), Special Collections (Myrtle Anderson-Smith) and George Washington Wilson Collection (Mary Murray), the Archivist to the Town Clerk (Judith Cripps), the Archivist to Grampian Health Board (Fiona Watson), and the North East of Scotland Library Service. Prints from the George Washington Wilson Collection of negatives held by the University Library are available to the public through the Library. Pictures without acknowledgement are from the author's own archive. For information on specific firms I would like to thank M.R.P. Fleming of John Fleming & Co. Ltd., Andrew Harvey of C. Davidson & Sons Ltd. and Isobel Smith of J. & J. Crombie Ltd. I am also very glad to have the chance to thank my family for their encouragement and for putting up with the disruption of family life that the preparation of this book entailed.

The industries described in the following pages were not the sum total of Aberdeen's economy in the period 1888 to 1913. They are simply a selection of industries that employed a significant amount of machinery. Almost entirely missing are small industries, the retail trade and the domestic economy. One can read between the lines and catch glimpses in the illustrations that social and working conditions were markedly different from those of today. I have not made an issue out of this, for it requires a complete text on its own. A few readers may remember these times but there can be very few alive today who worked in Aberdeen's industries during the years covered by this book. Many, though, must have had close relatives who did. If this account encourages anyone to bring out family pictures showing Aberdeen at work in a different era, it will have served a useful purpose. Among premises that eluded my search for interesting photographs were the extensive Kittybrewster Locomotive Works of the GNSR, the City Flour Mills in Causewayend, R. & J. Shinnie's Coachworks, John T. Clark's Carriage & Harness Works and the Spey Boot & Shoe Company. On reflection, there were indeed many others. I hope that readers with interesting material buried in some rarely opened album or box will consider it worth digging out and will show it to others.

As modern cities grow to look the same, one realises that the only Granite City in the world has a particularly special atmosphere and appearance. Surely, the more we appreciate the city's past, the better we shall look after the city of today. I hope that this appreciation will be enhanced by the unusual glimpses given here into one of Aberdeen's historic epochs.

Chapter 1 sketches the background from which the Aberdeen Mechanical Society emerged. The bulk of the book, chapters 2 to 7, describes the industries of Aberdeen that were visited by the Society during the first 25 years of its existence. The final chapter mentions industries outside the Aberdeen area that were also visited and discusses some of the topics of the day that attracted the attention of members. Looking through the industrial anatomy laid out in these pages won't tell one what made the city of Aberdeen tick, but it will certainly show some of the wheels that went round.

John S. Reid   Findon, September 1989

Aberdeen Mechanical Society Presidents from 1888 - 1913: R. Gordon Nicol (Harbour Office, from 1895 Harbour Engineer); James Smith (Bannermill); John Esson (Blaikie Bros. Footdee Iron Works, later Robert Gordon's College); James W. Thomson (Robert Gordon's College); Andrew Sproul (Blaikie Bros., later consulting engineer); R. Gordon Sharp (Great North of Scotland Railway, later Midland Railway); Cochrane Ketchen (Davidson's Paper Mills); Thomas Mowat (Works' Manager, Harpers Ltd.); James Mitchell (Harbour Office, dredging inspector); William Grant (Manager, Iron Grit Co. Ltd.); J. F. Drake (Great North of Scotland Railway); William Gauld (Blaikie Bros., later left Aberdeen); Samuel Milne (Corporation Gas Works); John King (Harbour Office, dredging inspector); James Mitchell (Foreman Engineer, Clyne Mitchell & Co. Ltd.); Walter Simpson (Plumber and allied trades); James Laing (Consulting Engineer, Major in First A.R.E.(V)); George H. Murray (Hall, Russell & Co. Ltd.); John Buchanan (Robert Gordon's College); Alex R. Horne (Robert Gordon's Technical College). Courtesy, Aberdeen Mechanical Society.

Nineteenth Century Mechanics
and the Aberdeen Mechanical Society

Introduction – 25 years of Industrial Aberdeen.

Twenty five years is a short time in the history of a city, yet it is long enough for a citizen to detect trends and changes. In Aberdeen over the period 1888 to 1913 the granite industry flourished, providing dressed stone for some of Aberdeen's best housing stock and generating a prosperous export trade; the shipyards thrived building steam trawlers, and the fishing industry thrived using them; the public services made far-sighted provision for the city's requirements into the twentieth century. These activities, however, neither started nor stopped within the chosen 25 years. What began in 1888, and is still vigorous, is an institution that deserves to be more widely known for the rôle it has played in Aberdeen's social and economic history – the Aberdeen Mechanical Society. Its activities during the first 25 years of its existence have provided the inspiration and the theme for this account. As will become clear, though, what follows in these pages is not a history of the Society but rather a glimpse of Aberdeen as seen by its members in the Society's early years.

Machinery as technology has been the prime interest of the membership, taking them deep into 'the works' of Aberdeen's commercial and civic ventures. Looking back into the Society's records, we see granite, textiles, papermaking, shipbuilding, railway engineering and many more of Aberdeen's industries through the eyes of those who played an important part in them. Their archives and other sources bring to light details of these industries that are not now well known, if they ever were. The facts and figures uncovered relate to a particularly interesting period in Aberdeen's history and one purpose of this book is to reveal them to a wider audience.

The vision and the competence of engineers in charge of a city's major industries make an important contribution to whether that city thrives or merely survives. Yet, few have heard of Aberdeen's public servants such as R. Gordon Nicol, William Dyack, G. R. Graham Conway, J. Alex Bell, Alexander Smith and Samuel Milne, all of whom shaped the town we know. Since many of the city's

undertakings in the years covered by this book are worthy of civic pride, it is time that these men were given credit for their contribution to local history, not forgetting the thousands working under them who built and ran the city's services.

Looking back over the centuries, it is obvious that as machinery has developed, so has society. Since the advent over two hundred years ago of useful steam power, the lifestyle of every citizen in the country has depended on the work done by machines. To give some historical perspective to the industrial scene in 1888, this introductory chapter looks briefly at the growth of mechanical technology in the nineteenth century and the conditions that led to the foundation of the Aberdeen Mechanical Society.

Developments before the Foundation

To gain an impression of the context in which the Society was founded in 1888, we must look right back to near the beginning of the nineteenth century. The industrial revolution was by then underway in earnest in Aberdeen. This meant not only that steam engines and powered machinery were being installed in the mills of Forbes, Low & Co. (cotton spinners at Poynernook), Hadden & Sons (wool spinners beside the Green, near Hadden Street), and others, but that mechanical principles were being applied to the development of almost every artifact of life, from agricultural tools to precision instruments. Many initiatives were made in Aberdeen to keep up with the times and in particular to improve technical education. One of these initiatives was a proposal in 1823 to found the Aberdeen Mechanics Society. This society was to provide education for operative and master mechanics and interested friends on subjects likely to be of benefit to them, particularly Natural Philosophy (i.e. Physics) and Chemistry. In the following few months the proposals were revised and implemented. In April 1824 the opening lecture was given to the Aberdeen Mechanics Institution, as it was called in revision, by William Knight, Professor of Natural Philosophy at Marischal College. Over 500 attended from a population of 45,000 and some 550 paid their 10/- membership subscription in the first year. Knight

View of 'Machinery in Motion' in the western annexe of the International Exhibition of 1862. Large beam engines can be seen in the centre and on the left; a small horizontal steam engine at front right.

began a course of 28 lectures which was augmented by 20 further lectures on Chemistry by William Henderson, also of Marischal College. The appetite of Aberdonians for self improvement was considerable.

Bodies like the Aberdeen Mechanics Institution sprang up all around the country. They encapsulated the spirit that was to push mechanics to the forefront of technology throughout the nineteenth century. By 1826 there were over 100 Mechanics Institutions in Britain, 27 of them in Scotland. Hundreds of men like Knight were saying, in speeches or in writing, *"that which distinguishes savage from civilised life"*, I quote from Knight's inaugural address, *"is the invention and application of machinery for procuring the necessities and comforts of life; and that, consequently, the pre-eminence of any people in civilisation is to be estimated by the state of industry and mechanical improvement among them"*. This message was taken to heart by technologists and romantics alike.

1888 was the 51st year of Queen Victoria's reign, a reign that deserves to be known as the Age of Mechanics. Today, it takes only a power failure to make us realise how important electricity is. In the nineteenth century it was mechanics that transformed society. On a large scale, the railway system spread across the country, giving people power they never had before to move themselves and their goods around. The quarrying and building industries expanded cities and roads, giving factories the power to employ people in such numbers as they had never done before. The shipbuilding industry supplied a tonnage of trading ships that gave Britain a power to trade that it never had before. Mechanics generated power, physically, socially and politically. On a smaller scale, the electrical wonders of the century like telegraphy, that spread communication across the oceans, and telephony, that brought direct communication between distant people, relied on precision mechanical components. The early gramophone was purely mechanical, as was the internal combustion engine. Mechanics penetrated all walks of life.

The 1851 Great Exhibition at the Crystal Palace, and its sequel in 1862 at South Kensington, brought home to the public that civilisation was judged by its mechanical prowess. Galleries of machinery were considered a gleaming tribute to the progress of Britain and many other countries, ranking of equal importance to the galleries of ornately crafted objects that characterised mid-nineteenth century social life. As the century passed, however, Britain relied too heavily on its reputation. There was a trade slump as

Late 1880s view of the newly erected Aberdeen Art Gallery and Industrial Museum (on left), the entrance to Robert Gordon's College and Gray's School of Art, the final location of the classes of the Aberdeen Mechanical Institution. The striking contrast between Peterhead and Kemnay granites in the facade showed well when this elegant corner of the city was uncluttered. Courtesy, Aberdeen University Library GWW Collection, no. C5559.

cheaper and better foreign machinery was produced abroad. Worse, the initiative for innovative machine tools and practices moved from Britain to the U.S.A., Germany and France. Such was the state of affairs in the late 1880s.

At home, the Aberdeen Mechanics Institution evolved during Victoria's reign, with ups and downs, from a society conceived to benefit operative mechanics to a body organising applied education over a wide range of subjects. Encouragement to turn an excellent voluntary organisation into a professional establishment was provided by the Endowed Institutions (Scotland) Act of 1878 and the Educational Endowments (Scotland) Act of 1882. As a result of these Acts, Glasgow's Mechanics Institution became in 1886 the Glasgow & West of Scotland Technical College; Edinburgh's, as the Watt Institute, was amalgamated with Heriot's Hospital to become Heriot Watt's, now a University. In Aberdeen, the Mechanics Institution spawned 3 bodies we take for granted. Most obvious is Robert Gordon's Technical College (now RGIT), though it did not develop directly from the Institution. Less obvious are

the Public Library and Gray's School of Art.

In 1881 the old Robert Gordon's Hospital reorganised itself into Robert Gordon's College, taking advantage of the Endowed Institutions (Scotland) Act of 1878. When I was a schoolboy passing through the gates of Robert Gordon's, there was a bronze shield on the large gateway inscribed *"This gate is the gift of the Aberdeen Mechanics Institute whose educational work was transferred 1882-84 to Robert Gordon's College, along with a proportion of the Institute's property and funds"*. By inheriting the work of over half a century, Gordon's was able to become quickly the centre of local technical education. Robert Gordon's Technical College was a development of this provision that came into effect on 1st January 1910.

The Mechanical Institution's impressive library and building in Market Street, now the Metro Hotel opposite Hadden Street, became the core of Aberdeen's free public library; its Art teaching transferred in 1885 to John Gray's splendid new building next to the recently finished Art Gallery and Industrial Museum (as it was initially called). Thus, although the Institution did not die until 1925, it had completed its allotted rôle. It had raised the consciousness of Aberdonians to technology and launched its activities to a wider public, but its dissipation had left Aberdeen's mechanics with no focal point.

Founding the Aberdeen Mechanical Society

In 1888, William Gauld, a draughtsman with engineers Blaikie Bros., urged the formation of a new society – the Aberdeen Mechanical Society whose object was to propagate mechanical science *"by Essays, Debates and Lectures, and visits to places of mechanical interest"*. This was to be a society for mechanical engineers of all interests to expound and discuss developments relevant to their own subject. The spirit of self and mutual improvement was still clearly visible.

In June 1888, Gauld and his friend Charles Hunter canvassed support for their proposed society and at a preliminary meeting 35 agreed to join. By October, such was the interest that a large and well organised Society was inaugurated, accumulating over 100 members and a full committee of 11 by the end of the first year. Subscriptions were 3/- per annum for ordinary members, 2/- for associates and 5/- for honorary members (cheap compared with the 1824 'Institution' prices). John Gray, who was a governor of Robert Gordon's and a director of Wm. M'Kinnon & Co. Ironworks, was a founder member. There were two Honorary Presidents. One was Rev. Dr. Alexander Ogilvie, Head of Robert Gordon's College, who was glad to offer their newly instituted mechanical class-room as the regular meeting point for the Society. This courtesy of the College to the Society has been continued for 100 years and is warmly appreciated by them. The other Honorary President was Charles Niven, F.R.S., Professor of Natural Philosophy at the University and a former governor of Robert Gordon's College. He gave the inaugural lecture on 16th October 1888 to a packed audience. Taking the chair was R. Gordon Nicol, engineer at the Harbour Office and the Aberdeen Mechanical Society's first executive president.

Niven concentrated on the future. He emphasised that foreign competition and trade slumps gave the *"spur of necessity"*, as he put it, to improvement. He naturally emphasised the educational rôle the Society

William Gauld, founder of the Aberdeen Mechanical Society. Courtesy of the Society.

could play *"a man is only half-educated who does not owe a considerable part of his education to himself"*, he said; he hoped that those involved in local industry would contribute their knowledge freely (without prejudice to trade secrets); he spent more than one third of his talk emphasising that all engineering was underpinned by the principles of physics. In particular, he stressed the importance of a theoretical understanding of energy conversion, highlighting the work of James Joule (after whom the unit of energy has been named the '*Joule*'). His talk was received with much applause and reported at length in the press.

But what was actually happening in mechanical engineering in 1888? On a large scale, the Forth railway bridge was nearing completion and the Eiffel tower was under construction. More pervasively, internal combustion engines, like today's petrol engines but running off gas, were developing in efficiency to displace the smaller steam engines; other small engines were also being improved, such as Dugald Clerk's two-stroke. Charles Parsons had made the key step in building a successful steam turbine that could drive an efficient electric power plant (though power stations did not use this technology

PUMPING MACHINERY OF EVERY DESCRIPTION.   DIAMOND WASHING PLANT.

TIN MINING MACHINERY.   HAULAGE GEARS.

WM. McKINNON & CO.,
Limited,

ENGINEERS, ...
IRONFOUNDERS, and
BOILERMAKERS . . . .

ABERDEEN.

SUGAR and RICE MACHINERY.   HYDRAULIC ELEVATORS.

ELECTRIC ELEVATORS.

ALL TYPES OF BOILERS AND ENGINES.

Speciality of STEEL RIVETED PIPING,
BY THE LATEST AND MOST UP-TO-DATE PLANT.

John Gray, whose political and financial influence shaped the educational facilities available to engineers in the 1880s, was a director of Wm McKinnon & Co. Founded in 1798, they are now Aberdeen's oldest engineering firm. This advertisement of 1907 shows their typical products of 100 years ago. Courtesy, Aberdeen City Libraries.

winter, talks were given at fortnightly intervals, soon becoming every 3 weeks. During the summer, visits were made on Saturday afternoons to local industry, initially at intervals of 3 weeks, later once a month. After the specialisation of the winter meetings, these visits showed members applied mechanics in the round. They were very well attended, 60 being a typical turn-out in the earlier years, more later on. The Society were frequently given the courtesy of a guided tour by the manager himself, and smaller firms sometimes kept their workforce employed for the Saturday afternoon to show the machinery in action. Summaries of the visits were reported in the *"Aberdeen Free Press"* and the *"Aberdeen Daily Journal"*, separate newspapers in those days. Some appeared in the *"North Daily News"*, a third paper that existed in 1891 and 1892. One firm being visited in 1892 were thanked by the Society *"for the great amount of trouble they had taken to make every detail clear to such an extremely curious set of men as engineers were"*. To this curiosity we owe many press reports of Aberdeen's industries.

Succeeding chapters describe the Aberdeen that was seen by the Aberdeen Mechanical Society members during their first 25

until much later). The bicycle, after over two decades of development with crank and pedal, was looking recognisably modern with the appearance of the Rover and Singer safety cycles. In tools and techniques a pilot form of electric arc welding had appeared and the advent of the oxy-hydrogen cutter was being given unexpected publicity by a spate of safe-breaking incidents. J. B. Dunlop made his first successful pneumatic tyre in 1888 and Otto Lilienthal was about to produce the first successful hang-glider.

It was to the innovations of mechanical engineering, usually on a small scale, and to local industry that the Aberdeen Mechanical Society was to turn its attention. During the

Professor Charles Niven, F.R.S., Honorary President of the Aberdeen Mechanical Society, who delivered their inaugural address.

years. I have drawn upon the press reports of these visits and supplemented them with detail and statistics from other contemporary descriptions. Long sections have not been quoted, but to keep the descriptions as accurate as possible I have tried to retain the original language where it was precise. A quick look through the places visited will show that the indelibly associated *"twal mile roon about"* brings in the Seaton Brick and Tile Works, and papermills along the Don and at Peterculter. Indeed, the twelve miles is stretched to include industries at Kemnay, Inverurie and Ellon.

Shortening the rail link to Aberdeen, one of the piers of the Forth bridge rises in the first year of the Aberdeen Mechanical Society to give Engineering a high public profile. Courtesy, Aberdeen University Library, GWW collection no. A1013b.

Early ornamental medallion of the Aberdeen Mechanical Society, featuring steam engine inventor James Watt. Courtesy, Aberdeen Mechanical Society.

2

Granite and Textiles

Granite

The granite industry was entering its strongest phase when the Aberdeen Mechanical Society began their visiting programme one hundred years ago. By the beginning of the twentieth century it employed some 9000 men directly and an estimated 30,000 more indirectly. About 90 firms were involved in Aberdeen, mainly dressing, polishing and sculpting the stone.

Among the quarries around Aberdeen, Kemnay matched Rubislaw in size. Its silver-grey stone, with light tinges of brown and glistening mica inclusions, has built many of Aberdeen's majestic city buildings, including the Town House, the Marischal College frontage and extension, His Majesty's Theatre and the Public Library, Queens Cross Church, and numerous others. The visiting Society arrived by Great North of Scotland Railway at the private Paradise Siding of Kemnay quarry. From there, granite waggons were normally drawn up a steep incline by steam winch, to be loaded at the top of the quarry. Mr John Fyfe, who had started the

Kemnay Quarry, circa 1890, showing granite being lifted by blondin, the steam house and a floor level steam derrick crane. Courtesy, Aberdeen Art Gallery & Museums, Aberdeen City Arts Department.

Kemnay quarry in 1858, designed and erected the first modern aerial cableway in the country, for raising stone out of the pit-like hole. These cableways became a common sight in the Aberdeenshire quarries, being nick-named blondins after Charles Blondin who had thrilled the crowds in Aberdeen in 1861 with his tight-rope walking expertise.

Members were lowered to the main quarry floor by blondin to inspect quite a range of cranes, rock-drills and pumping gear all driven by high-pressure steam piped from a large boiler house at the quarry top. It was for John Fyfe that the first steam derrick-crane in Great Britain had been made. In 1897, the biggest crane in Kemnay (by M'Kinnon & Co., Ironworks) could lift 15 tons around a large radius. In spite of the problems with steam leaks and having to run the boiler house even when few machines were needed, the use of steam power at many quarries persisted long after the advent of electric motors, because the system had been proven to work under adverse conditions.

During a visit in 1906, members of the Aberdeen Photographic Society accompanied the Mechanics to record the scene on glass-plate negatives. Back at the top of the quarry, inspections were made of all the plant: engines that hauled waggons round the quarry's own rail system by steel cables and worked the blondins; DC dynamos for arc and other lamps; stone breaking and crushing machinery; and the well-equipped workshop. Although quarrying had a grim reputation for hard manual labour, there was said *"to be nothing more up to date in quarrying"* than John Fyfe's enterprise. In 1906, over 300 men were employed.

It was natural that the first granite yard to be visited was the Aberdeen Granite Works of A. Macdonald & Co., occupying a four acre site in Constitution Street, now more familiar as the home of B & Q stores but then in the shadow of the Bannermill. In the late 1820s, Alexander Macdonald had revived the art of granite polishing, which allegedly had been lost since ancient times. When Mr Fergusson, the works' manager who showed them round in 1890, had joined the firm in 1841 there were about 10 journeymen and a few apprentices. From a small beginning, this yard spawned

Steam derrick cranes and blondin cableways at the stonemasons' sheds of Kemnay Quarries, circa 1900. Courtesy, Aberdeen Art Gallery & Museums, Aberdeen City Arts Department.

the huge monumental trade for which Aberdeen had become so well known abroad.

The firm specialised in Celtic crosses, urns, capitals and pedestals, models for each of which were first made in plaster of Paris. They had received prizes in many International Exhibitions and all the chief monumental erections for members of the Royal Family, including the tomb of the Prince Consort, had been designed and built by them. When visited, in the outside yard beneath a crane capable of lifting in excess of 15 tons, a large doorway in red polished granite *"of magnificent proportions and generous dimensions"* was being erected prior to despatch to Buenos Aires. During a return visit in 1895, members saw in the turning shop large granite pillars 17 feet long by 2 feet 6 inches diameter, being turned for the new Théâtre Opéra Comique in Paris. Visitors to Paris can, I believe, still see the results. Actually, one need only go to the courtyard of Aberdeen Art Gallery to see turned granite pillars at their best. Like almost every yard of its day, steam drove the machinery; in this case a 150 horse power engine supplied by a boiler 7 feet high by 30 feet long, with of course the obligatory chimney venting the furnace smoke.

Another well mechanised yard was the Froghall Granite Works of Charles McDonald, founded in 1877 when McDonald

returned from America. After a time this yard specialised in preparing imported granite from Norway and Sweden using machinery driven by a 200 horse power steam engine installed in 1900. (Notice the distinctive Norwegian granite among the Art Gallery courtyard pillars). Nearby, at the Jute Street Granite Works, Arthur Taylor presented to the Mechanical Society in 1900 the first two pneumatic hammers that had been used for granite work in this country. They had been employed by him to carve the statue of Hygieia and four lions that commemorates the presentation by Elizabeth Duthie of the park that bears her name to the City of Aberdeen, and its opening by H.R.H. Princess

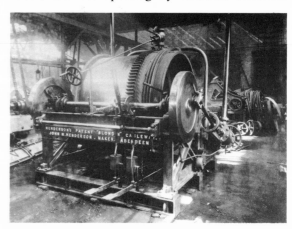

Blondin Cableway winding gear, 1894. Courtesy, John M. Henderson & Co. Ltd.

The first pneumatic tools to be used on granite in Britain, carving Hygieia's four lions in Arthur Taylor's granite yard. Courtesy, Aberdeen Art Gallery & Museums, Aberdeen City Arts Department.

Beatrice in 1883. Hygieia, the goddess of health, is represented in her traditional form as a virgin holding a cup from which the symbol of health, a snake, drinks. The four lions in pink granite, one must suppose, represent the strong citizens in the park (in the pink?). Hygieia herself stands some 30 feet on an ornate Corinthian column and pedestal that is

John Fyfe, from a painting by J.S. Sergent. Courtesy, Aberdeen Art Gallery & Museums, Aberdeen City Arts Department.

Hygieia and four lions in the Duthie Park, the first granite statue to be carved with pneumatic tools.

a monument not only to health but to a new era of granite carving.

Pneumatic tools quickly spread through the granite industry, and elsewhere. Small tools greatly increased the output of sculptors accustomed to mallet and chisel. When applied to the stone, the tool ate away superfluous material with some 1500 strokes per minute, and flowers, fruit, heraldic shields, regimental crests and such designs were produced as easily as from marble. The accompanying photograph taken no later than 1906 shows their extensive use in James Taggart's works in Great Western Road, where about 50 men were employed. Taggart himself, who was married to the author's great aunt Eliza Reid, oversees the operation on the right. He

About two thirds of Taggart's workforce in the pneumatic tool shed, circa 1905. Taggart himself oversees, on the right. Courtesy, Aberdeen City Libraries.

Mechanical traverse crane spanning a typical granite yard shed, 1894. Courtesy, John M. Henderson & Co. Ltd.

Trial erection of a large ornate piece at an unidentified granite yard, circa 1900.

Granite polishing, circa 1900.

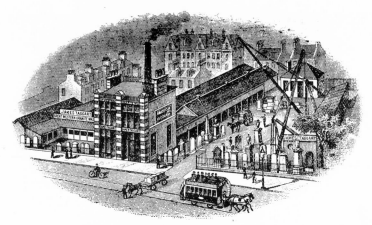

James Taggart's granite yard, from an advertisement. Courtesy, Aberdeen University Library.

was a prominent Town Councillor and as an Honorary Member of the Aberdeen Mechanical Society was an active participant on their excursions in the early 1900s. John M. Henderson (Jnr.), also active in the Society, was a son-in-law and Taggart's strong connections with Aberdeen's industries no doubt helped him become Lord Provost from 1914 to 1918.

Textiles

At the end of the nineteenth century, granite and its associated industries had taken over from textiles as Aberdeen's largest employer. Big names in textiles of the early nineteenth century, such as Milne, Cruden & Co. (linen manufacturers), Gordon, Barron & Co. (cotton spinners), had disappeared in the 1850s. However, the Bannermill, founded in 1826, was still going strong *"within sight of the whitening breakers and within hearing of the deep booming of the German Ocean"*, as the press described it. *"The bracing salt breezes of the North Sea sough and whistle to the accompaniment of the spindles"*, all 75,000 of them in 1898 when the Aberdeen Mechanical Society paid its visit. Under the management of Robinson, Crum & Co. 90 bales of American cotton, each weighing 450 pounds, were separated, washed, carded and spun into hanks every week.

The mill had an extraordinarily large beam engine which had been modernised several times since it was first built in 1839. A great trundling flywheel of 60 tons weight, one of the largest in the country, smoothed the 832 horse power used to drive the mill's machinery. An ingenious *"electric stop"* arrangement allowed the drive to be stopped from six different places in the factory in case of accident. The mill was the first in Scotland

to be fitted throughout with automatic water sprinklers as a fire precaution, not for the exclusive benefit of workers but also *"to effect an enormous saving in insurance"*. About 600 hands were employed. In spite of the apparent prosperity, this most northerly mill in the country eventually could not compete with the Lancashire giants who both spun the cotton and wove flannel and other cloth. It closed early this century, though its activities are still commemorated by the adjacent street name *"Cotton Street"*, along which the cotton used to arrive and depart.

THE ULTIMA THULE OF THE COTTON INDUSTRY.

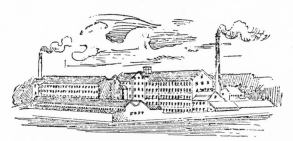

The Bannermill, from a press sketch at the time of the Aberdeen Mechanical Society's visit in 1898, representing the mill a few decades earlier.

Jute was a material of rising importance in the second half of the nineteenth century. It was easily dyed and took bright colours; it mixed with flax, tow, wool and silk, and was largely used for upholstery, schoolbags, coat linings and in the manufacture of slippers, blankets and caps; it was the carrying material of the world. The Aberdeen Jute Works was begun in 1875, perhaps spurred by the success of Dundee's earlier transfer from linen to jute. When visited in 1899 it handled 13,000 bales of raw jute annually, imported from London, Dundee or direct from Calcutta. Each bale weighed 400 pounds. The long silky

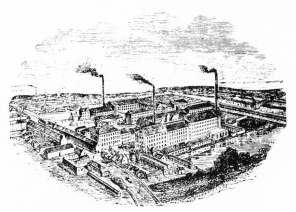

Broadford Mill, from a sketch published in 1889, representing the mill when it had a mill-pond. Courtesy, Aberdeen City Libraries.

strands were heavily impregnated with resinous matter and needed more pre-treating than cotton before being ready for one of the 2,600 spindles in the spinning mill. For many years the manager, James Ducat, was an Honorary Member of the Aberdeen Mechanical Society. The works (located at Sunnypark in Froghall, at the end of Jute Street) lasted about fifty years before being closed.

The Broadford Mill began its life a little before 1810 as a linen manufactory. The introduction of powerloom weaving there by John Maberly & Co. in 1824 made it one of the earliest powerloom linen factories in existence. It was sold in 1832 to Richards & Co. who built up an extensive flax spinning, weaving and finishing works that survive to this day, though with a different product. When visited in 1890 the eight acre site employed about 3000 hands producing from the raw material linen sheeting and towelling, sail canvas, tent cloth, hose web and similar fabrics.

It was the motive power of the works that particularly interested the Mechanics. Nine boilers supplied high pressure steam to five engines totalling 1200 horse power. If anyone wishes to see a superbly restored horizontal mill engine not unlike the kind of engine that one could find at Richards and elsewhere in Aberdeen, they should visit the recently reconstructed main hall of the Science Museum in London. There such an engine is kept going daily by an engineer, under steam. At Richards the steam engines are, of course,

no longer there, but a steam engine house dating to about 1910 still stands and its tall rectangular brick chimney beside Hutcheon Street is a listed building. As well as a modern horizontal Corliss valve engine, the works possessed an ancient pair of beam engines that drove the whole powerloom department with great reliability. Prior to being woven, the flax was treated by *"heckling machines"*, *"carding engines"* and quite an array of mechanical apparatus before being spun, either dry for thicker yarn or wet for finer threads. It was taken to a separate works, then at Rubislaw, for dyeing. Among the special looms, Jacquards were programmed with punched cards to reproduce intricate patterns, and a number of others *"of specially strong make"* were used to manufacture canvas fire hose, for which Messrs Richards & Co. *"had long been famed"*. They continued to be well known for these products until quite recently but now have abandoned weaving to concentrate on producing yarns, mostly synthetic.

The textile for which Aberdeen has been noted for three centuries or more is wool. Fine Aberdeen woollen hosiery was admired in the seventeenth century. Alexander Hadden & Sons, whose nineteenth century factory was so near the centre of town, employed between 300 and 400 hands in hosiery, and were also large spinners of woollen and worsted yarns. They closed at about the same time as the Bannermill. Kilgour & Walker Ltd., woollen manufacturers at the Berryden Mills,

The Broadford Works 1989, stretching from the massive mill on the left to the rectangular chimney of the powerhouse on the right, appears across George Street as a red brick island in the Granite City.

Large tandem horizontal mill engine at Richards' Broadford Mill, probably circa 1910. Courtesy, Richards p.l.c.

visited in 1900, also had an extensive stocking knitting department. Besides this, they took the wool through all stages from the raw material, including dyeing and spinning, in the process of making fabrics such as wincey, skirting, kersey, plaiding, blankets and tape.

The largest woollen manufactory in the

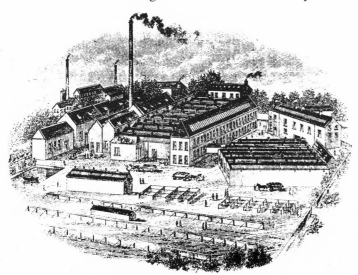

Kilgour & Walker's mill between Berryden and George Street, from their letterhead. Courtesy, Aberdeen University Library.

area was that of J. & J. Crombie at Grandholm Mills, a firm still well known in Aberdeen. When the buildings were first visited in 1890 some of them had been standing for over a century. They were erected as flax mills for Leys, Masson & Co. but successive trade recessions towards the middle of the nineteenth century caused the failure of this large firm in 1848. After some interest by Alexander Hadden, the buildings remained in disuse until taken over by J. & J. Crombie of Cothal Mills, Fintray, in 1859. The premises were enlarged to cover five acres and employed between 700 and 800 people in 1890.

In all, 17 carding engines, 12,000 spindles and over 200 power looms were marshalled to produce overcoatings, suitings, trouserings and other fine cloth *"well known in the first-class London, Continental and American warehouses"*. The visitors passed wool washing vats, wool dyeing machines and the wool drying department where the machines were heated by steam pipes laid under the floor. The wide mill lade, over a mile long and a legacy of Leys, Masson & Co., supplied

The largest powerloom shed in Britain, at the Grandholm Mill in 1880. Note that the drive shafting runs under the floor. Photograph by George Washington Wilson, courtesy J. & J. Crombie.

15,000 cubic feet of water per minute to a water wheel that *"was held to be the largest water wheel in the world"* when it was constructed. It was 25 feet in diameter, 20 feet 6 inches wide, weighed 100 tons and generated 200 horse power as it ponderously rotated at 8 revolutions per minute. Such were the statistics of nineteenth-century mill power. When it was installed it would have produced more power than several of the best steam engines put together. However, even Leys, Masson & Co. were keen to develop steam power to supplement the climatic uncertainty of falling water. For their part, J. & J. Crombie had

installed two horizontal Corliss valve steam engines providing another 300 horse power. Commercial electricity was still in its infancy in 1890 and there were no *"electric mains"* of any sort. The most advanced firms, such as Crombies', generated electricity for electric light in the principal rooms. They also generated the gas they required at the works.

By 1907 they had expanded to nine acres, 16,492 spindles and 260 looms, but still employed about 800 hands, two-thirds of them being women. We get a glimpse of a firm in a transitional stage of technology. They had installed more powerful engines all round. Their great water wheel was a historical wonder but this had not saved it from demolition in 1905. It was replaced by a Hercules water turbine occupying about a twelfth of the space, using much less water and producing one and a half times the power. The steam engines had been replaced in 1902 by the latest tandem compound engine and the entire finishing department converted to run off electricity using electric motors of 5 to 15 horse power to drive each line of shafting. In total, well over 150 kilowatts of electricity could be generated on site at 220 volts for their own *"mains"* system. This was happening in factories all over the country, though Crombies had been quick off the mark. Because the carding, spinning, weaving and

Grandholm Mill, nineteenth century. Courtesy, J. & J. Crombie.

Warping machines in the Grandholm Mills. Courtesy, Aberdeen Journals.

Chief engineer James Milne (with notebook) consults the German lubricant specialist beside the new horizontal steam engine at J. & J. Crombie, circa 1903. The large flywheel with multiple rope drive is just visible in the rear left. Courtesy, J. & J. Crombie.

other machines did not generate their own power, a radical change in energy supply such as the advent of electricity could be accommodated relatively easily. The old machines were simply driven from the old shafting by different means. The next step, of dispensing with the shafting and belts and installing new machines with built-in motors, could be accomplished when the machines themselves became obsolete.

The electrification that took place in the decades 1890 to 1910, first for lighting and then for power, was not simply a matter of riding the fashion. It was driven by hard-nosed economics. Mills, with their large buildings, fine materials and the usual long working hours of the age, needed plenty of artificial light. Machinery had to be improved continually to combat the falling prices for finished material and the rising expectations of quality. Mills were, therefore, obvious places for early electrification. In contrast, granite quarrying continued to use steam powered technology at the quarry face long after electrification became a possibility, because the capital cost of changing could not be justified.

3

Electricity and Gas

Electricity

Prior to the 1880s, useful electricity was available only in small quantities. Batteries of modest efficiency ran the telegraph network, powered the newly invented telephones, plated silverware, rang bells and did sundry other chores. In the 1880s two mechanical developments changed that scene. The first was the evolution of dynamos that generated kilowatts of electric power. The second, curiously enough, was the development of the vacuum pump, whose improvement made the humble electric light bulb a possibility. Filament light bulbs had been devised forty years previously but the filaments kept burning out because of the very small amount of residual air in the bulb. It was the development of a pump that could produce an exceptionally good vacuum that allowed Joseph Swan in England and Thomas Edison in America jointly to patent useful carbon filament incandescent lamps that revolutionised the interior of our factories and houses. (Our modern light bulbs with their tungsten filaments and inert gas filling are an early twentieth-century development).

The carbon filament lamp was quite a robust item but not very efficient. The candle power of a lamp was a measure of the amount

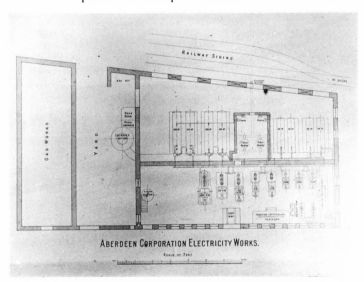

Plan of Aberdeen's first public electricity generating station, that was inaugurated in 1894. The engine hall, fronting onto Cotton Street, contained 10 steam-driven dynamos at the time this plan was drawn (circa 1900); the rear hall, 8 furnaces and steam boilers, with a combined flue outlet leading to a 154 foot high chimney. Courtesy, North East of Scotland Museums Service.

of light given out compared with that from a standard sperm candle weighing six to the pound and burning at a certain rate. The 16 candle power of a typical lamp was achieved by consuming the same amount of electricity as a modern 60 watt bulb, but the light was not nearly as brilliant. For example, a 16 candle power lamp on a wall 8 feet away from someone writing a letter gave only the same illumination as a single candle placed 2 feet away. It was also much more yellow than a modern bulb because the filament reached a temperature of only 1900 degrees Celsius compared with the 2300 degrees of a tungsten filament. To make matters worse, black carbon gradually became deposited on the inside of the glass, dimming the light given out. In spite of these disadvantages, the electric lamp became ever more popular. Curiously enough, Philips, one of the pioneer manufacturers of the mass produced carbon filament lamp, have begun to make them again in substantial numbers after a break of over 50 years. The ambience created by their soft yellow light has found favour once more.

The bigger works around Aberdeen began to install the new dynamos, wiring and lamps in the early 1890s, as indicated in the previous chapter. Besides filament lamps there were also very effective carbon arc lamps. When Harpers Engineering works at Craiginches went electric in 1895, they put in 55 arc lamps giving 75,000 candle power of light, driven by their own large gas engine. The press reported that the amount of gas used was so trifling that "*it would only light up a corner of the works were it put through the burners in the usual way, instead of being converted into electricity through the engine and dynamo*". These lamps took one third of a kilowatt each and would be quite useful in a modern studio. With Harpers offices "*nicely lighted up by 35 incandescent lamps*" their installation was the largest of its kind in Scotland.

By then, the Town had appreciated that a public utility would benefit the citizens at large. The municipal Cotton Street generating station was opened early in 1894. It had been built on gasworks ground at a cost of £21,500, under the supervision of the indefatigable Alex Smith who had been manager

Inaugurating the electrification of the city's tramways, December 1899. Courtesy, Aberdeen City Libraries.

of the gasworks for some 25 years. It was intended that there should be no rivalry between the gas and electricity departments. Upon the opening night of 28th February, the public gathered in large numbers in Union Street and Castle Street, where 10 arc lamps had been hung as the initial stage of a street lighting plan that was to spread up Union Street and down branch streets. There was *"a great volume of cheering"* when Lady Provost Stewart threw the inaugural switch to light the streets, for Aberdeen was said to be only the second corporation in Scotland to install electric street lamps and the first to build its own station. (Glasgow had taken over a pre-existing private venture).

The Corporation sold electricity at 7 pence per unit, about two hours wages for a worker, though later a complicated sliding scale was introduced. The '*unit*' used was the same as our existing unit, namely the '*kilowatt-hour*'. From the beginning, electricians used the metric unit of power, the '*kilowatt*', nearly equal to one-and-a-third '*horse power*'. With charges so high, it is not surprising that customers used the electricity to run lights, which took only moderate power, and not machinery that needed a lot of power. Electric lights were clean, simple to use and service, and didn't smell or burn up the oxygen in a room. Demand increased, albeit slowly at first due to the expense, and the Mechanical Society were assured during their visit to the Cotton Street station in 1894 that the works were built for expansion. Their initial capacity was about 300 kilowatts.

In 1898 detailed plans were drawn up to electrify Aberdeen's horse-drawn tramway after the Corporation had acquired the assets of the Aberdeen Tramway Company. In the following year, within a few days of the end of the century, the first electric tram took passengers from St. Nicholas Street the length of George Street to Woodside. During the following three years the remaining nine miles of existing tramways were electrified. 500 volts DC was the supply used, the maximum allowed by Board of Trade regulations. One effect of the new tramways was to stimulate the demand for electricity to run machinery.

Looking back on developments in Aberdeen at the beginning of this century, it is clear that many departments of the Town's adminis-

Erecting a wing of the Dee Village power station, September 1901. Note the cranes typical of those that were used to erect much of Aberdeen's granite building stock. Courtesy, Aberdeen City Libraries.

tration were staffed with far-sighted and highly competent men. The gas and electricity supplies were no exception. Mr J. Alex Bell was the city Electrical Engineer, Honorary Vice-President of the Aberdeen Mechanical Society from 1902 - 04, Honorary President from 1904 - 06. In 1899 he set afoot an ambitious scheme to build a large power station that would see Aberdeen well into the twentieth century. Adjacent to the power station would be a new tram depot and workshop, a logical siting to reduce power transmission losses to a minimum.

The site of Dee Village (at the foot of Crown Street) was close to the railway station coal yards, close to the water source of the river Dee and close enough to Aberdeen's commercial and residential areas. In the opinion of *"Bon-Accord"* magazine in 1900, the site was too close at hand for, their columnist argued, it was objectionable to have *"chimney-stalks belching forth their fumes in the midst of a residential area"*. Nonetheless, it was purchased by the Corporation for £8000 and cleared early in 1901. £28,000 were spent over the next three years on generating station buildings covering about two acres. The station itself was opened in March 1903 and the tramway depot finished some twelve months later. With the help of the accompanying photographs, let us look round with the Aberdeen Mechanical Society when they visited the Works in 1903 to see the scale of the City's biggest investment in twentieth-century technology at the time.

In the engine room, 126 feet long by 62 feet wide, were eight combined steam engines and dynamos, another two having being housed earlier in an adjacent temporary wooden erection. The plant could supply 3,810 kilowatts for lighting, heating, power and (tramway) traction purposes. Steam engines require cooling condensers to make the most of the steam power. These condensers were supplied with water by two pumps housed in an underground chamber on the bank of the Dee. After being heated by the condensing steam, this water was returned via the Ferryhill Burn which flowed in a culvert right through the Works. The condensed steam ran into an underground hot-well, from where it was fed back to the boilers.

The boiler house was even bigger than the engine room. Behind the chain grate stokers seen in one of the photographs were 10 large Babcock and Wilcox boilers, each capable of producing 15,000 pounds of steam per hour at the high pressure of 160 pounds per square inch. Feedwater for the boilers was stored in cast-iron tanks holding 115,000 gallons on the top of the *'economiser house'* (more anon). Very cheap-quality coal was brought by carts to the works each morning and transported by electric conveyor belt from the storage bunkers at up to 20 tons per hour to the furnaces. Later a railway line was laid to bring coal to the site.

J. Alex Bell, City Electrical Engineer who directed the electrification of the tramways and the building of the Dee Village power station. Courtesy, Aberdeen City Libraries.

Engineers installing the steam engines and dynamos in the power station engine room, January 1903. Courtesy, Aberdeen City Libraries.

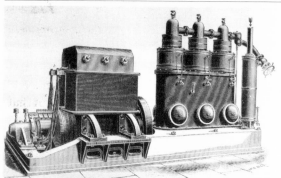

Contemporary textbook engraving of one of the triple-expansion Willans steam engines used in the power station, coupled to a DC generator.

The power station furnace room ready for firing, March 1903. Note the scale from the size of the man. Courtesy, Aberdeen City Libraries.

The great power station chimney, 200 feet high by 14 feet in diameter, rises in August 1901. The houses behind, at the foot of Crown Street, still stand. Courtesy, Aberdeen City Libraries.

Front of the newly erected Corporation Electricity Works on Millburn Street. Courtesy, Aberdeen University Library George Washington Wilson Collection, no. D2318.

Every big steam plant in Aberdeen had at the base of its tall chimney a *'Green's Economiser'*, a device hardly known about in a works these days. Edward Green patented the first version in 1845 and his firm of E. Green & Son at Wakefield made them for a worldwide market. Our cut-away picture is by Professor Jamieson who, in the early 1890s, designed the economiser for the electric lighting plant of the (old) Royal Infirmary in Aberdeen at Woolmanhill (visited by the Aberdeen Mechanical Society in 1893, see chapter 7). The economiser stopped useful heat going up the chimney. It consisted simply of a set of cast-iron tubes placed in the flue passage. Through these tubes the boiler feedwater passed to be preheated. The pipes very soon became coated with soot and were generally scraped continuously by mechanical scrapers driven by an electric motor. The power station had probably the biggest economiser in town, two 480 tube units occupying a house 49 feet long by 35 feet wide. One side effect of feeding the boiler with hot water was a significant reduction in boiler corrosion. Another was that the economiser condensed out some of

the noxious fumes emitted by the smoke stack, but I have not seen that put forward as any justification for its use.

The Mechanics were naturally entranced by the engine room, which had a glass gallery floor to allow an operator insulated access to the lighting and traction switchboards. The Corporation were particularly pleased with the associated cable subway, shown in one accompanying photograph. *"A unique feature…it is believed that this cable subway is the longest of its kind in the kingdom"*, as *"Bon-Accord"* magazine put it. Installed at a cost of £18,661, eight feet high by four feet eight inches wide, it made its way up Crown Street before narrowing and turning into Langstane Place. It then proceeded to Holburn Street nearer the surface with a horseshoe profile. For 1500 yards, electricity was conveyed to the central, northern and western city districts without the unsightliness of overhead cables. The subway was built because it could easily house new cabling that was bound to come with the growing demand for electricity, whereas simply burying the cables was a recipe for repeated street disruption.

The subway was lit by means of 8-candle-power lamps every 21 feet apart and the atmosphere within was kept *"in a pure and cool condition"* by two substantial electric fans that drew warm air from the generating station engine room. The fans themselves exhausted the stale air, and the further of the two was situated in the distribution chamber at the end of the cableway beneath a curious piece of iron street furniture that I passed for thirty years before realising its function. It is located on a small traffic island in front of the Odeon Cinema at the west end of Justice Mill Lane.

Underneath the cable subway in Crown Street was (and still is) a second tunnel that formed part of Aberdeen's new sewerage system that is described in chapter 6. Both were sunk in a trench at the same time, with considerable disruption to that part of the town. At its greatest depth, beside Academy Street, the trench had to be made 30 feet deep to maintain a smooth gradient in the sewer.

The subway was designed to carry over 50 cables bearing 440 volts DC. However, an Act of Parliament of 1890 prohibited power stations from supplying customers with more than 300 volts, in the interests of safety, and an ingenious 3-wire system was adopted whereby half the voltage was given to one house and half to a neighbouring house. By

Green's economiser; sketch by Professor Andrew Jamieson based on his design for the electric lighting plant of the Aberdeen Royal Infirmary.

this means the station achieved some of the well-known economy of distributing at higher voltage without needing a DC transformer to reduce the voltage to the customer. This was not an invention of a canny Aberdonian but was standard practice in those days. A few years earlier, 110 volts had been the usual supply, since this was the highest voltage for which incandescent lamps were normally manufactured. The original decision to choose 110 volts was made by Thomas Edison, as a compromise dictated by technical problems with the lamps. In America, the electricity companies did not push for a higher and more economical voltage when the change could have been made and they are now stuck with the less satisfactory 110 volt mains supply. Old practices sometimes have far reaching consequences.

Another feature of the power station was the battery room located underneath the offices in the central block. There a very large supplementary battery, or more accurately a floor covered with batteries, could supply 440 volts at 220 amps for 10 hours. The battery

Aberdeen's cable subway, 1902. Courtesy, Grampian Regional Council, Department of Water Services.

Aberdeen Corporation's electricity shop, not long after it was opened in 1910 at 244 Union Street. (The original print is unsharp). Courtesy, North East of Scotland Museums Service.

was charged when demand was light and used when it was heavy. It was also used, at least in the first instance, to supply the power on Sundays. Another smaller feature of the station was a culvert where cabling practices could be tested. Public electricity supplies were still in their infancy and common lead-sheathed, 3-core, paper-insulated cables were subject to alarming and unpredictable explosions. Work at the test facility showed that the cause was water being absorbed by the insulation at the junction boxes, and a wiring technique was devised for ensuring safety.

Scottish Hydro Electric p.l.c. still occupy the Aberdeenshire granite office block in Millburn Street that was the Corporation Electricity Works. The original steam engines

Motorised service vehicle for maintaining the tramway overhead cabling system. September 1903. Courtesy, North East of Scotland Museums Service.

Joinery workshop at the Aberdeen Corporation generating station and tramway service depot, Dee Village, circa 1910. Courtesy, North East of Scotland Museums Service.

were replaced by more efficient steam turbines, eventually with a capacity of 57.25 megawatts. Even these were insufficient for the energy-thirsty twentieth century. The plant was phased out after the National Grid was established in 1948, being used as a reserve source when the load was high in winter. In February 1969 it was closed down, the tall chimney subsequently demolished and the turbine hall replaced by an office block.

Round the corner in Crown Street one can see the large arched entrance to the 1904 tram depot and workshop, now walled up. Four lines of pits gave access to the undersides of the trucks for repair; hydraulic rewheeling apparatus made good for wear and tear; a paint shop dealt with damage and rust, and a motor-tower waggon was ready for emergency calls in connection with tramway breakdowns. Without the trams, Aberdeen's suburbs would not have developed as they did.

Gas

The most visible feature of a city's gas supply is the gasholder, the reservoir holding a few days' gas supply to smooth out the irregularities of production and demand.

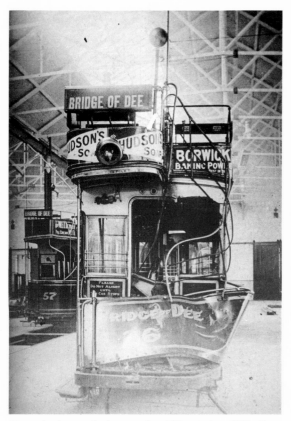

Trams in the repair depot at Dee Village, circa 1910. Courtesy North East of Scotland Museums Service.

A disappearing landmark. A view across the Trinity Cemetery of the great Gallowhills gasholder that was built in 1892 - 1894.

Many citizens rightly admire the ornate Kemnay granite facades of Aberdeen's principal buildings but who could raise any enthusiasm for the Gallowhills gasholder? Yet, it was a remarkable undertaking by the Town Council, representing the largest structure of its type built in Scotland at the time, using over 2000 tons each of concrete and steel during its building from 1892 to 1894.

By way of introduction, it is worth recalling that the generation of gas from coal for the purpose of lighting had first been demonstrated one hundred years before by Scotsman William Murdoch, an engineer for Messrs. Boulton & Watt, then working in Cornwall. The Aberdeen Gas Light Company erected the first local works at Poynernook in 1824, manufacturing oil-gas during the first four years and charging 40 shillings per 1000 cubic feet, about a fortnight's wages for many. In 1828 they began the manufacture of coal gas at 15 shillings per 1000 cubic feet. The Aberdeen New Gas Light Company was formed in competition in 1844, generating coal gas from the Sandilands site. Two years later the two companies amalgamated and in 1871 an Act of Parliament transferred the Company's assets to the Town Council. Since that date, gas production almost doubled every 10 years and the cost slowly fell. By 1903 it was 3 shillings per 1000 cubic feet.

To accommodate this rising use of gas, the town decided to construct one massive new gasholder at the Gallowhills, with a capacity of 3,750,000 cubic feet, to supplement the four existing holders at the Cotton Street works that could store between them

2,140,000 cubic feet. Consumption was then averaging a bit over 1,000,000 cubic feet per day, more than doubling this in the depth of winter. The choice of one large holder was based on the good principle that if one increases the size of the holder the volume stored increases proportionately more than the surface area, which is the part that actually has to be built. One has to stop this process when the materials used no longer have the strength to support the structure. The economy of scale clearly worked well in this case, for the cost of the Cotton Street holders was £19-6-9 per 1000 cubic feet whereas the Gallowhills holder cost only £3-12-6 per 1000 cubic feet.

When the Aberdeen Mechanical Society inspected the structure in the summer of 1894, they were given a detailed account by Alexander Smith, the City Gas Engineer and an Honorary Vice-President of the Society. Underneath the visible three-lift holder is a huge tank 40 feet deep by 210 feet in diameter made of concrete reinforced by iron bands every 2 feet. This was a progressive use of reinforced concrete, replacing traditional brick construction, making it the largest concrete gasholder in Scotland at the time it was built. The walls were 6 feet thick at the base, tapering to 3 feet 6 inches at the top. About 100 of the Corporation's own men were engaged in the excavations and the whole

Alexander Smith, City Gas Engineer, courtesy John Lovie.

Finishing off the interior of the Gallowhills gasholder, 1894. Courtesy, Aberdeen Art Galleries & Museums, Aberdeen City Arts Department.

tank took over a year to make. The steel work for the holder and the guide framing that rises 123 feet above ground were contracted to a Glasgow firm. A large welded-steel supply pipe was laid from the Cotton Street generating station. It says a lot for the planning, the workmanship and the maintenance of the plant over decades that this major piece of engineering lasted the entire remaining working life of the coal gas industry in Aberdeen. Many people have noticed it who might otherwise have not, thanks to its prominent position next to Pittodrie football stadium.

The Society revisited the completed gasholder in September 1894 and continued on to the gas plant itself. Producing town gas from coal was not a simple matter. At the heart of the process, coal was heated in a closed chamber called a retort so that all the volatile components evaporated, leaving behind coke. However, the hot gas that was given off contained much more than 'coal gas' and hence the unwanted constituents had to be separated by physical and chemical means. First, the crude gas was passed over cooling

condensers that extracted the tarry and liquid components. It was then sucked off to washers and scrubbers that took out the ammonia and some other water-soluble gases before finally being led into the purifying plant. Here it was passed over chemicals such as iron oxide and slaked lime which combined with the noxious hydrogen sulphide, carbon disulphide and other unwanted compounds. At every stage the materials to be handled were unpleasant at best and quite hazardous at worst. The solids generated dust and grime, the liquids smelt foul and the gas was explosive! In such an atmosphere the more that could be done by machinery, the better.

In the all important retort house there were (in 1898) 432 horizontal D-shaped retorts, each 9 feet long, 25 inches wide and 14 inches high, arranged in a double bank down the centre of the 400 feet long building. The retorts were heated by gaseous firing to 2000 degrees Fahrenheit (1100 degrees Celsius). Each took a charge of about two and a quarter cwts. (115 kilograms) of coal eight times a day, giving a total coal consumption of about

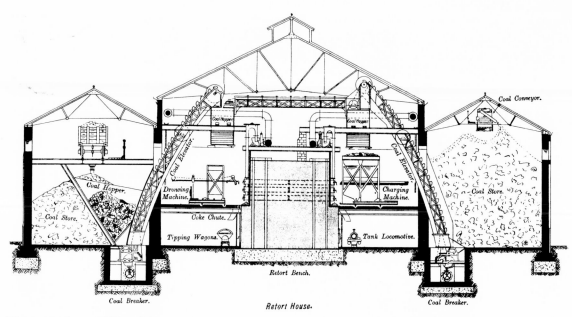

Diagram by Samuel Milne of the retort house. Courtesy, Aberdeen University Library.

65,000 tons per year. Not all the retorts were continuously used, either because some collapsed from time to time or because some were kept in reserve when demand was light. Prior to 1886, the whole of the coals used by the Aberdeen gasworks were taken by horse and cart from ships' sides or the railway station at a haulage cost of 10 pence per ton. In 1883, Parliamentary powers were obtained to construct a railway between the Gasworks and the Harbour Commissioners' rails, and from 1886 onwards two powerful locomotives were employed in the haulage. At that time the unloaded coal was broken into suitably sized lumps *"by old men with hand hammers at a cost of 5 pence per ton"*.

One of West's retort charging machines at the Aberdeen Gas Works, circa 1905. Courtesy, Aberdeen City Libraries.

When the retorts were loaded by hand it was hot, arduous and fatiguing work. A gang of three had to charge 48 retorts per shift of 8 hours, with each retort taking about 7 minutes. One of them swung open the retort door and flames burst forth, lighting up the dark bare building with a weird and lurid glare. The three speedily raked out the fiery hot residual mass, which fell through holes in the floor to be quenched with water by other men. The gang proceeded to recharge the retort, their object being to get the door of the fiery furnace closed as soon as possible. One man would rhythmically throw shovelfuls just beyond the front while the other two loaded the firing shovel, an instrument with a long half cylindrical end and an even longer handle. Upon the word, the leader grasped the handle of the scoop and the other two lifted the middle by means of an iron rod. The whole was run smartly in towards the back of the retort, overturned and pulled out empty. The performance was gone through twice for each retort, taking care that the coals evenly covered the retort floor. This scene was drawn by a contemporary writer visiting another works, but it would not have differed much between plants. To keep going all the 366 retorts installed at the time of manual loading in Aberdeen required a total of 136 stokers and 68 assistant stokers. The works were operated 24 hours a day.

In 1890 the Aberdeen Gasworks introduced mechanised coal breaking machines, three of which were placed on either side of the retort bench. Railway trucks delivered the

The new purifier house, erected in 1903, in which the job of emptying and refilling chests of chemicals was mechanised. This job was previously undertaken by 7 men with horses and carts. Courtesy, John Lovie.

coal directly to the mouth of the coal breakers, each being then set in motion by its own attached 10 horse power steam engine. The engine also drove the elevator that lifted the broken coal to a large hopper placed on the girders 20 feet above the retort house floor. It was then ready to drop into the new stoking machinery, made to West's patent and installed at a cost of over £5000 at the same time as the breaking machinery.

Aberdeen was the first Corporation in Scotland to use labour-saving machinery for charging and discharging an entire bank of retorts. There were two charging machines, each weighing 13 tons, and two withdrawing machines, each weighing 7 tons, one on either side of the line of retorts. West's stokers travelled on rails parallel to the retort bench, driven by endless overhead cotton ropes receiving power from a pair of 40 horse power steam

Holmes patent washer-scrubber, at its erection in 1897. Courtesy, John Lovie.

The interior of one of the two gas exhausting pumps installed in 1896 and driven by the steam engine in the rear. The front is 4 feet across and the pump delivers 80,000 cubic feet of gas per hour. Courtesy, John Lovie.

engines. After about 10 years, West's pneumatic stoking machines superseded the original versions. The picture confirms that they were heavy and simple in construction, as was required when working amid clouds of smoke, dust and an intense heat. With one driver they could charge from 45 to 50 retorts in an hour.

One man who was conspicuous in forwarding improvements in the gasworks was Samuel Milne. He rose to become outdoor assistant to Alexander Smith and subsequently succeeded him as manager. In 1905 - 1906 he was President of the Aberdeen Mechanical Society and from 1911 - 1913 President of the Aberdeen Association of Civil Engineers, for he was active in both societies. Smith and Milne together planned a new exhauster, installed in 1896, a new scrubber in 1897, a new purifier house in 1903 and a separate retort house erected in 1899 - 1901 containing 36 new-style inclined retorts. In late 1907, Samuel Milne pointed out to the Gas Committee of the Town Council that demand had risen by 100 million cubic feet over the past five years to a record level of 725 million cubic feet per year. In spite of the installation

Building some of the inclined retorts (above) in 1901. These retorts (below) were visited by the Aberdeen Mechanical Society during their erection. Courtesy, John Lovie.

Samuel Milne, successor to Alexander Smith as City Gas Engineer. Courtesy, Aberdeen University Library.

of the inclined retorts, capable of producing at least 400,000 cubic feet of gas per day, the plant was stretched to capacity. In passing, it is worth remarking that this increased use of gas in the era of electrification owed little to improved gas lighting (which had taken place) but resulted from the displacement of the traditional kitchen range by gas stoves and open grate fires by gas fires. The latest gas generating technology was the vertical retort, into which coal was fed continuously and automatically at the top while coke was withdrawn at the bottom. However, the technology was not sufficiently proven commercially to merit investment and Samuel Milne urged the Corporation to establish a Carburetted Water Gas Plant.

This plant was to be built in a portion of the building recently relinquished by the Electricity Department upon taking out of commission the original Cotton Street generating station. The new plant, consisting of two sets each of 750,000 cubic feet per day capacity, would occupy only a small space and could be fired up at short notice to cope with demand fluctuations. It would cost only half as much

as inclined retorts of the same capacity. The water gas was a mixture of carbon monoxide and hydrogen obtained by passing steam through white-hot coke. This gas by itself burnt with an almost invisible flame and had to be mixed with another gas rich in illuminants, produced in the 'carburettor' by spraying mineral oil onto red-hot bricks. The mineral oil vapour was decomposed into gaseous fragments within the third component of the plant, the 'superheater'. The crude gas mixture was passed through scrubbers, condensers and tar extractors in the usual way before being collected in one of the existing gasholders set aside for the purpose. It was finally discharged through a meter into the exhausting and purifier line of the coal gas plant.

The Aberdeen Mechanical Society visited the completed carburetted water gas plant in March 1911 after an explanatory talk by Samuel Milne. The economics of carburetted water gas production were attractive and many Corporations added a similar facility to their gasworks after the First World War. Samuel Milne pressed on with the modernisation of Aberdeen's gasworks and began the first phase of a conversion to vertical retorts in the period 1913 to 1915, an early initiative in this field. Under his direction Aberdeen had completed the conversion to a large vertical retort installation by 1928. It was the vertical retort building that dominated the gasworks skyline until the end of coal gas production in the 1970s.

CHAPTER

4

SHIPBUILDING & THE HARBOUR

Shipbuilding

The only shipyard visited by the Aberdeen Mechanical Society in its first twenty five years was Aberdeen's largest – Hall, Russell & Co., Aberdeen Iron Works. Since their

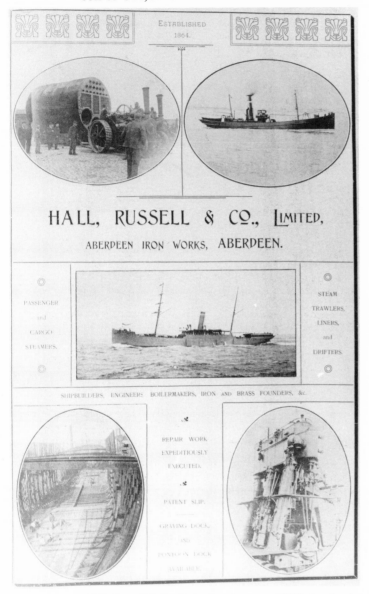

Hall, Russell & Co. Ltd. advertisement of 1907 showing the range of work undertaken. Courtesy, Aberdeen Public Libraries.

foundation in 1864 they had expanded to the capacity of the area then available, about 5 acres. When in full swing some 1200 hands were employed in *"engineering, boiler-making, iron and brass-founding, coppersmith and plumbers' work, ship-building, boat-building and all the usual departments"*.

The Society's visit of 1891 was divided

over two separate Saturdays, one to see the ships and another the engines. They were first guided by the manager, Mr Anderson, into the office block where the main attraction was the plans for the Aberdeen White Star Liner *"Thermopylae"*, then under construction. A handsome model, said to be 1/96th scale, was

The elegant SS "Thermopylae". She was visited by the Aberdeen Mechanical Society while under construction. Courtesy, Aberdeen City Arts Department.

in the process of completion by Mr Wishart for the owners, Messrs George Thompson & Co. of Aberdeen. A contemporary half-model of approximately twice this scale is now on display in its original mahogany ornate mirrored cabinet in the Aberdeen Maritime Museum. (The S.S. *"Thermopylae"* should not be confused with the famous clipper *"Thermopylae"* built in 1868 by Walter Hood & Co. for the Aberdeen White Star Line and sold by them in 1890). Next the Society passed to the joiners' loft and boat-building shops that provided the fittings and finishing which made a vessel functional and attractive within. Every ship was custom built from the keel upwards and we are not surprised to find these facilities spacious, and well equipped with power tools. Some six men were employed in French polishing alone.

Out in the yard, five vessels on the stocks were typical of Hall, Russell's commissions. 1891 was near the beginning of the steam trawler era that was to bring prosperity both to the shipyards and to Aberdeen's fishing industry. Three steam trawlers of 110 feet in length were in various stages of construction. Beside them was the almost completed hull of the *"Induna"*, a vessel of 200 feet being built for John. T. Rennie & Sons to augment their regular fleet used in the South African trade. The final ship was the *"Thermopylae"* herself. She was 362 feet in length by 44 feet beam, and would weigh 3200 tons when complete with engines and boilers. Accommodation was being built for 50 first-class passengers and 300 third-class. The music room, dining saloon and state rooms were all *"to be fitted up in excellent style"* and the vessel lighted with electricity, quite a new development.

Two months later the Society returned to examine the engine shop and in particular the engines for *"Thermopylae"*. Hall, Russell & Co. built every engine needed for its vessels. *"Thermopylae"* was to be fitted with 3000 horse power of the latest *'triple-expansion'*

Typical triple-expansion marine engine of the period by Hall, Russell & Co. Ltd.: this one for the collier SS "Aberdon" (210 feet long, launched 1911). Courtesy Hall, Russell & Co. Ltd. and Aberdeen Town House Archives.

marine engines in which the steam was used three times for greatest efficiency. This type of engine was developed in the 1880s and dominated ships' engine rooms for 40 years, before being replaced by steam turbines and diesel engines. First, steam went into the high pressure cylinder, then the intermediate pressure cylinder and finally the low pressure cylinder. The pistons in each cylinder all drove the same crank-shaft, just as the four pistons in a modern car engine do. In Thermopylae's engines the crank-shaft was made from steel 15 inches in diameter and the final steam cylinder was almost 6 feet across. To match this scale of engineering there were two main steam boilers, each about 14 feet high by 20 feet long and weighing 60 tons. Three furnaces at both ends of each boiler required

stoking and one can imagine that it must have seemed like the devil's own work to make full steam ahead as *"Thermopylae"* plied its regular route between London and Australia. In addition there was a smaller auxiliary boiler. After all this effort *"Thermopylae"* had a tragically short life, for she ran aground near Cape Town in 1899 never to be refloated.

Marine boilers near completion in Hall, Russell's boiler-shop. The largest is 16 feet in diameter and 11 feet 7 inches long, designed to work at a pressure of 180 p.s.i.. Courtesy, Hall, Russell & Co. Ltd. and Aberdeen Town House Archives.

When the Society finally returned to Hall, Russell & Co. in 1907 they found a yard even more mechanised than before, though employing a similar number. A compressor supplied air to pipework led all over the yard for pneumatic tools used for chipping, caulking, drilling and rivetting. These worked on the same principles as pneumatic tools used in the granite industry. A hydraulic installation supplied hydraulic riveters, cranes, a manhole punch, guillotines, angle shears and a powerful plate bending machine. Steam power was generated for the yard by two marine boilers each 14 feet in diameter.

Two modern gas-fired furnaces had been erected the year previously, one that could take bars up to 50 feet long and the other for plates 20 feet long by six and a half feet wide. The Corporation electricity supply was used for the latest electrically driven tools. A new part of the boiler shop had a 30 ton overhead travelling electric crane and a glass roof under which, according to the press *"the light is as good as that available in the open"*. This roof can be seen in one of our pictures. In another picture can be seen the blacksmiths' shop with forges, three powerful steam hammers, welding facilities and vertical drills.

With all this equipment, Hall, Russell's continued to attract orders for large vessels. In 1910 the elected president of the Aberdeen

Huge steam engines line one wall of Hall, Russell's engineshop. Courtesy, Hall, Russell & Co. Ltd. and Aberdeen Town House Archives.

Towing the hull of "Intaba" to the shear-legs for fitting out. Courtesy, Aberdeen City Arts Department.

full-plate glass negative now among the University's George Washington Wilson collection. The engines were impressive too, with six boilers driving 3000 horse power of machinery. One of the engines can be seen in the accompanying picture from Hall, Russell's own archive. It is said by those who remember the *"Intaba"* that she was particularly well fitted out.

Mechanical Society was George H. Murray, one of the senior staff of the yard. That summer he arranged for the Society to inspect their most prestigious contract – the hull of the largest steamer ever built in Aberdeen until that time, the 386 foot *"Intaba"*, another John T. Rennie & Sons vessel nearing completion on the stocks and destined for the East African route. It was, apparently, the first passenger ship to be constructed on a new system, the Isherwood system, that saved over 200 tons of weight in this instance. Its launch was quite an event that year, captured on a

One of the triple-expansion steam engines built for SS "Intaba" (1910). Courtesy, Hall, Russell & Co. Ltd. and Aberdeen Town House Archives.

The blacksmiths' shop at Hall, Russell & Co. Ltd.. The steam hammers down the centre are between 9 and 10 feet high. Courtesy, Hall, Russell & Co. Ltd. and Aberdeen Town House Archives.

1910: launching SS "Intaba", the largest steamer ever built in Aberdeen up to that date. Courtesy, Aberdeen University Library, GWW collection no. D2340.

Harbour Works

As long ago as 1810 (or the late 1820's according to some), the management of the harbour was vested in a Board of Commissioners whose administration and accounts have since been kept distinct from the municipality. Various Acts have reconstituted the Harbour Board since that time and conferred extensive powers upon them to develop the port facilities as they have thought best. The harbour that we see today must represent a thousand million pound investment (at current prices) by the citizens of Aberdeen, spread over more than two centuries, to convert an unexceptional estuary into a port appropriate for modern commerce. During the period we have been looking at, 1888 - 1913, the harbour improvements were impressive, as befitted a city that was commercially diverse and energetically managed.

A quick look at the harbour trade around 1905 shows imports and exports closely related to many of the activities discussed in these chapters. Imported were the raw materials for Aberdeen's industries: coal, timber, iron, granite, esparto grass, cereals, sugar, feedstuffs, salt, chemicals and over 10% of all fish landed in Britain. Exports were dominated by stone, paper, preserved food, oatmeal, hides, soap, candles, flax, woollen and jute manufactures. It was, with local variation, the pattern of Britain at work a century ago, as every schoolchild used to learn. The picture underplays the importance of the service industries in the local economy but, as far as the harbour was concerned, these commodities dictated the facilities required and supplied the money for improvements. At its simplest, trade was increasing, vessels were becoming larger, deeper, faster, and more numerous. Over the 20 years prior to 1905, harbour trade had doubled and during the 25 year period covered here, over a million pounds (1900 prices) were spent by the Harbour Board on dock improvements.

The first president of the Aberdeen Mechanical Society was R. Gordon Nicol, an Aberdonian by birth, who was promoted to Harbour Engineer in 1895. A visit by the Society in 1889 examined the harbour machinery. Though little is recorded of what was seen, they must have visited the Central Hydraulic Station opened in 1885 that powered the Graving Dock gates, the swing bridges at the entrance to Victoria Dock and other facilities. Large steam driven pumps were also installed

R. Gordon Nicol, 1904. Courtesy, Aberdeen City Libraries.

there to empty the Graving Dock of water. This machinery was housed in a prominent Corennie granite building adjacent to the Graving Dock, with a round brick chimney 100 feet high at its West end. From 1900 onwards, R. Gordon Nicol became a prominent figure in Aberdeen's engineering circles, for he directed several major alterations to the harbour. He was both a mechanical engineer and a civil engineer, becoming president of the influential Aberdeen Association of Civil Engineers in 1904 while also Honorary President of the Aberdeen Mechanical Society. He was an outspoken proponent for more engineering education in the town.

A prolonged period of Harbour improvements was initiated in the 1890s, with a particular interest being taken by Provost Daniel Mearns when he was Honorary President of the Aberdeen Mechanical Society. The great Regent Bridge Improvement Scheme involving some six years of work was mooted in 1894 and finally begun in 1899. The old swing bridge spanned the mouth of the Upper Dock, the innermost dock adjacent to Market Street. With the introduction of large steamships, the old bridge spanned too narrow a gap (48 feet) and at 15½ feet wide could not cope with the land traffic either. Deepening the inner dock had threatened to undermine its foundations and hence in this instance the

Harbour Board had little option but to act. What they did showed considerable faith in the long-term future of the harbour. The bridge was a busy thoroughfare. A census had shown that 1450 people and about 350 carts travelled per hour across the Regent bridge at the busiest times, access being directly opposite Marischal Street. The new bridge was designed to carry unlimited pedestrian and vehicular traffic, and twin track railway lines supporting the heaviest locomotives and trains on both tracks at once. The bridge was 156 feet long by 45 feet wide, five feet wider than Marischal Street.

To allow ships into the upper dock, the new bridge was pivoted about two-thirds along its length, the short arm allowing the railway curves to be laid in the restricted space on the south side. The basic structure weighed 500 tons but had 140 tons of iron blocks added to the short arm so that it remained level when swung round. The operation of the bridge was brilliant in its simplicity. A hydraulic jack in the supporting pier lifted the bridge with a force of 750 tons on

Celebration on the new Regent Bridge: possibly when King Edward and Queen Alexandra came to Aberdeen in September 1906 on a semi-state visit. Courtesy, Aberdeen Harbour Board.

Building the new Regent Bridge, circa 1902. In the foreground is the hydraulic chamber with the lifting jack in the centre. The walls are of dressed Kemnay granite. Courtesy, Aberdeen Harbour Board.

one large hydraulically supported steel ball pivot. The slewing round was accomplished by two massive steel arms attached to the underside of the bridge and operated by hydraulic engines, moving in exactly the same way as a human arm opens and shuts a door. Steadying rollers prevented the structure rocking. The bridge opened or closed smoothly in about one minute at the touch of two levers, one for lifting and a second for swinging.

There were duplicate means of perform-

ing all the operations, including supporting the bridge on its pivot. A gas engine was provided to drive the hydraulic machinery should the electricity supply fail. Safety railings were incorporated for *"children of tender years who, without guardians, crossed the bridge in large numbers"*. When the Aberdeen Mechanical Society visited the almost completed bridge in 1904, Councillor James Taggart, well known for his wit, proposed a vote of thanks to R. Gordon Nicol for his lucid explanation, ending *"he was sorry the King was not coming to open the bridge, but Mr Nicol had done the next best thing in getting the Mechanical Society to inspect it"*. (Some years later Mr Nicol's daughter Catherine was to marry Sir James Taggart's son Edwin, but I doubt whether the Mechanical Society engineered that. Edwin Taggart went on to manage the great Engineering Works of John M. Henderson upon the sudden death of Henderson and his wife in 1925).

The improvement scheme also entailed a new deep water quay wall 600 feet long faced with ashlar granite, a large quayside two-story storage shed with travelling roof cranes for loading and unloading, and a complete new, wide entrance to the upper dock. I must admit that I do not normally give a second thought to a wall but when R. Gordon Nicol designed a wall, we should not be surprised that it is still solid almost a century later. (The whole improvement scheme, including the bridge, was designed and administered from harbour head office at a cost of £120,000). Here is how he went about it.

The walls were built of solid granite masonry laid on a foundation of concrete granite-faced piers each 14 feet wide by 12 feet long. No fewer than 100 of these foundation

The completed Regent Bridge in the foreground, with the incomplete new Regent Quay transit shed on the left; circa 1905. Courtesy, Aberdeen City Arts Department.

piers were sunk to the rocky bed, an average depth of 21 feet below the existing dock bottom. Before any stonework was built for the walls, however, each pier was loaded with iron weights amounting to 300 tons and upwards, and if the load was successfully carried without subsidence for a few days the pier was considered properly founded. The masonry was built of the largest rubble stones embedded in cement mortar to withstand the strains and rough usage of ships, individual stones weighing from 3 to 5 tons each. This is aptly known as *'Cyclopean masonry'* the whole forming a mass with no straight lines of

1906: work in full progress removing the Point Law tongue. Courtesy, Aberdeen harbour Board.

weakness. The walls were faced with dressed Kemnay granite and a heavy granite cope. In all 1,200 feet of walls were built to a maximum height of 47 feet but only about 10 feet of this was visible above the waters of the dock, the remainder never being seen. Mr Nicol added *"should it be desired at any future time to convert the present wet docks into tidal docks, where ships can come and go at any state of the tide, these walls will admit of this being done without the enormous expense of reconstructing them."* Of course, the whole harbour is now tidal.

Regent Bridge and Quay facilities lasted about 70 years before the pressures of oil-related traffic and new kinds of cargo dictated a major development of this part of the harbour. In the 1970s, the bridge was taken down, the North abutment removed (with great difficulty) to widen the inner dock entrance; Regent Quay itself was clad in sheet pile wall when additional depth was created in the dock, and the old quayside shed replaced by one more suited to modern cargo handling techniques.

Two other schemes for the long-term benefit of the harbour were undertaken soon after the Regent Quay scheme. As a result of a massive mid-nineteenth century effort to re-route the Dee, the river now enters what might be considered the body of the harbour at Point Law. If you go to the end of the South Esplanade East (called Mearns Quay) you will see that Point Law terminates in a substantial deep water quay some 200 feet long

Building the new Point Law wharf in 1906: top – open steel shoes are laid on the soft gravel and mud.; middle – interlocking piers are built upon the shoes using pre-cast concrete and sunk into the ground; bottom – the piers are finished in dressed granite and covered over. Courtesy, Aberdeen Harbour Board.

linking the Deeside quay with the Albert Basin quay. In 1905 Point Law ended in a long, narrow shoal tongue of land that tended to reflect waves across and into the main docks. The tongue also projected well into the desirable navigation channel and increased the turbulence of the Dee water discharging into the harbour, to the hazard of shipping. The Point Law wharf itself was almost entirely occupied with wooden fish-curing premises that were busy all year, but particularly so during the herring season.

In 1906 an operation was mounted to remove 400 feet of the protruding tongue by hydraulically cutting and dredging away 95,000 cubic yards of clay, shingle and sand. The new Point Law wall was built on interlocking piers sunk into the clay and gravel so that the whole structure would be strong enough to act as a breakwater even in the severest storm. The accompanying four pictures illustrate the scale and the phases of this work. The Point Law quay that one stands on today is a modern cap over the end of this work, made to take the weight of large tanks for petroleum products.

In 1910, 80 members of the Aberdeen Mechanical Society were taken out to the working vessel *"Viking"* anchored in the navigation channel. A major project to deepen the channel was underway. Previous efforts had involved dredging and the lifting of large boulders deposited by the glacier that had once come down the Dee valley. Now bed-

The rock-smashing vessel "Viking", used to deepen the channel bed in 1910. Courtesy, Aberdeen Harbour Board.

rock stretching northwards from the Torry shore had been reached. In such circumstances it was usual to break up the rock by means of electrically detonated explosives placed by divers in holes drilled in the rock. R. Gordon Nicol had a better idea.

On board the *"Viking"* the Aberdeen Mechanical Society saw a new rock-breaking plant working on the principle of a pile-driver. A 40 foot long steel forging weighing 22 tons was tipped with a conical point of special steel. It was held supported just above the bed of the channel by a tall tripod and suddenly allowed to fall under its own considerable weight. About 10 strokes were sufficient to break up the bed to a depth of 2¼ feet. One steam engine on board raised the pointed battering ram while another manoeuvred the vessel by hauling on some of the six anchor chains. About two acres had been broken up by the time of the visit, quite an area. Two feet of additional depth may not seem very much but the rock itself had to be shattered into small enough fragments for the grab dredger to carry it away. In all it is estimated that 35 acres were cleared at the remarkably modest cost of £30,000. After watching the rock-smasher in action, Mr Nicol invited the party to inspect the new shear-legs just erected (on August 22nd, 1910).

The capability of the new shear-legs being displayed, most likely upon commissioning in 1910 with one of the boilers of SS "Intaba".

Many Aberdonians will remember the shear-legs. They were impressive for their sheer size, even though one had never seen them working. In fact they were equipped with two drums, one of 100 tons lift and the other of 30 tons lift, both operated by one 100 horse power motor. A second motor of equal horse power allowed the rear leg to traverse forward while the front two legs pivoted. By this means the whole pyramid lent beyond the edge of the quay so that weighty boilers and engines could be lowered directly into a vessel being fitted-out. The new legs had been specially commissioned by the Harbour Board to be ready for the S.S. *"Intaba"*, whose equipment was on the limit of capacity for the old legs. The accompanying photograph shows the new legs beside the old ones, in what may have been an inauguration ceremony lifting one of Intaba's new boilers. The old legs remained in position alongside for decades afterwards.

The Harbour Commissioners were rather pleased with their in-house reinforced concrete pile-making plant that had produced the Point Law abridgement and, in 1911, the new River Dee Dock no. 1. The Aberdeen Mechanical Society were invited there to inspect the *"interesting operations of considerable magnitude"* in that year. In the following year a return visit to the harbour was occasioned by the new (steel) floating dry dock that was to take over from the old concrete and granite graving dock opened in 1885. This old dock, although 512 feet long, had been something of a failure due to the imperfect knowledge at the time of its construction of how to make concrete walls that could resist seawater under pressure. The chemical action of the seawater on the imperfect concrete had made parts of it porous and prone to crumble. Lessons had been learnt but its cost of £48,000, about a whole year's revenue for the harbour at that time, was never recouped. To provide reliable facilities for cleaning, painting and repairing the fishing fleet a pontoon dock had been installed in the Albert Basin in 1899. It was 126 feet long by 37 feet wide within, with a lifting capacity of 425 tons. Another pontoon was added in 1905. The new dock 310 feet long with a lifting capacity in excess of 5,000 tons was therefore the largest of three. A conspicuous sight in the harbour, it was well used for almost 50 years.

All these visits have given us a good sample of the more important harbour improve-

Post 1910: both sets of shear-legs can be seen in the background and Regent Bridge in the foreground. Courtesy, Aberdeen Harbour Board.

ments of the period, seen through the eyes of local visiting engineers. (The Point Law works were inspected by the Aberdeen Association of Civil Engineers and not by the Aberdeen Mechanical Society). Contemporary judgment was that Aberdeen could rightly boast of its harbour based industries and facilities. I believe posterity concurs that they were a credit to the enterprise of the Aberdeen Harbour Board. Of course not every venture was equally successful, witness the 1885 graving dock, and it is worth concluding with a brief description of one project that never came to fruition.

In 1889 the inventive William Smith, Harbour Engineer prior to R. Gordon Nicol, put forward a proposal for a small boat harbour and promenade pier to be built in Aberdeen's main bay. Smith considered the bay an underused resource of the town. Swimming enjoyed some popularity but during the preceding 21 years, 15 people had been drowned and about 240 rescued from serious danger by the Town's official *"Rescue"*, a strong swimmer of exceptional courage who patrolled the beach. Pleasure boating was based on the river Dee, with some craft suitable for venturing into the bay during fine weather. Smith's proposal to encourage swimmers, boating, fishing and other pleasurable uses of the bay was a pier of 900 feet in length on cast-iron pillars, containing a circular bathing station (with bandstand) and terminating in a small boat harbour 300 feet long by 100 feet wide built of granite masonry in cement mortar. Smith cited 25 other towns that had built promenade piers and estimated the cost at £26,000. In spite of its attraction the scheme was not developed, apparently for financial reasons. Now, 100 years later, the foreshore is probably more appealing than in Smith's day. The sewage farm (mentioned in chapter 6) has long since gone and various industries that used to taint the fresh air have closed down or changed their ways. Perhaps the time is now right to bring Smith's objective of improving the amenities of the bay itself into focus again, even if we do not use his solution.

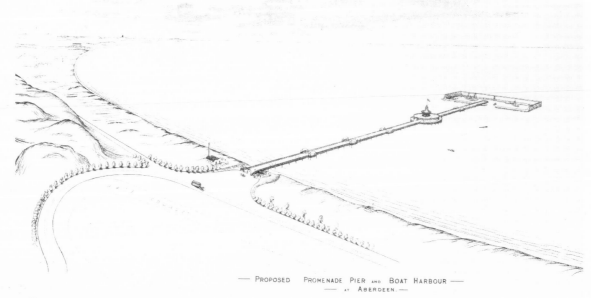

— PROPOSED   PROMENADE PIER AND   BOAT HARBOUR —
— AT ABERDEEN. —

William Smith's proposal of 1889 to build a promenade pier and small boat harbour in Aberdeen bay. Drawn by R. Gordon Nicol.

Paper Mills and Flour Mills

Culter Paper Mills

The paper mills around Aberdeen merited more visits by the Aberdeen Mechanical Society than any other local industry, a dozen during the 25 years covered. Of these dozen, four were to the Culter Paper Mills, considered as one of the best-managed and most successful companies in Aberdeen. Founded in 1751, they were the longest-running of our large local mills. Their apparently sudden demise in 1981 after over 200 years of prominent trading serves as an Awful Warning, if one were needed, that past success is no guarantee of future success. The site, containing so much relevant local history, deserved to be preserved at least in part as an industrial museum, rather than suffer conversion entirely into an estate of Barratt houses.

At the beginning of the nineteenth century paper was made everywhere in single sheets. To improve productivity, considerable effort and expense were devoted in France and in England to developing a continuous papermaking machine. By 1807 a fairly satisfactory machine that promised to be a commercial success had been patented by the Fourdrinier brothers. The first such machine in Scotland was bought in that year by the Culter Mills from Bryan Donkin, the principal engineer involved in its development and now recognised as one of the most expert mechanics of the early nineteenth century. The Fourdrinier machine, in which paper is initially formed by running pulp from a vat onto a vibrating endless fine-mesh wire cloth, was to be the basis of the standard papermaking machine from then on. The Culter Mills investment was even more notable because their machine was driven by the first Boulton and Watt steam engine installed in a papermill in Scotland. The 20 horse power steam engine was purchased second-hand from Brown, Chalmers & Co. at Craiglug near Aberdeen, for whom it had been built in 1803. As a result of this investment, the Aberdeen Journal used machine-made paper for the first time on 26th August 1812.

It may be wondered why paper mills bothered with steam engines in the early days, since a plentiful supply of water was a prerequisite for the papermaking process itself. The answer was that the steam engine provided reliable power throughout the year, with only modest and predictable maintenance and moderate cost. Many of the old beam engines kept going for over 50 years. Although water for a water-wheel was free, the expense and the upkeep of the associated dam, mill lade and sluices could be considerable. At times of flood there was the risk of costly damage and at other times, the risk of drought. Later in the century, the total steam horse power at a mill usually exceeded the available water power.

By the middle of the nineteenth century the Culter Mills turned out about 15 tons of paper per week. After several changes of ownership, from 1865 they were managed by the Culter Paper Mills Co. Ltd., who set about a programme of investment and expansion. By the time the Aberdeen Mechanical Society first visited them in 1890, they ran off about 60 tons per week and, according to the Press, were *"amongst the most complete of their kind in the United Kingdom, no expense having been spared in making both buildings and machinery perfect"*. They specialised in engine-sized writing paper (see later), bank vellum, cartridge and tinted papers, tinted pulp boards, embossed, duplex and burnished envelope papers. One eye-catching speciality for which they were the sole producers was a paper tinted differently on either side.

Envelopes were a particular speciality, two machines producing some 70,000 per day. One of these machines had been designed and made at the works by Mr Robertson, the Company's engineer. Another speciality was high quality deckle-edged paper (simulating the effect of hand-made paper) produced by a system patented by Mr James Johnstone, the manager of the mills. This paper had been selected *"from that of numerous competitors"* for printing one of the books of the year, D.C. Thomson's *"Barbizon School of Painters"*. *"The Times"* and other nationals especially praised the quality of the book's paper. This investment and development certainly supports the Press contention that *"the Company is noted all over the world for its excellence"*. Indeed, the art paper market drove considerable investment by the mill in the 1890s, with a new papermaking machine

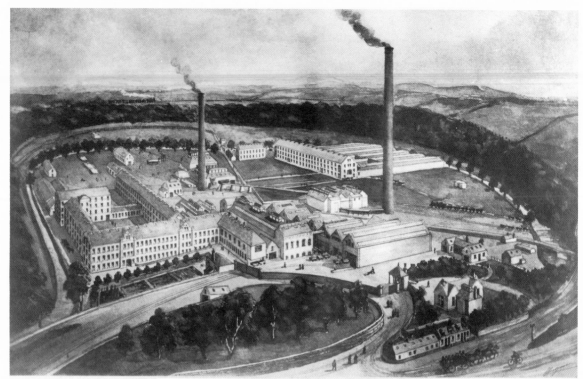

Founded 1751.

The Culter Mills Paper Coy. Ltd.

Culter papermills in the late nineteenth century. Courtesy, Aberdeen University Library.

of 100 inches width replacing one of the original machines, and new coating and polishing machinery occupying a four-storey building 200 feet long. Even so, by 1900 the firm still had orders in excess of its production capacity, though the falling price of paper generated smaller profits to fuel further development.

The bulk of the papermaking machinery was supplied by William and George Bertram of Edinburgh, the remainder being put in by James Bertram & Sons, Leith Walk Foundry. The two main machines, producing paper 72 inches wide (prior to 1896), were powered by two W. & G. Bertram compound steam engines of 250 horse power each. There were, besides, twenty steam engines for driving various machines throughout the mill and these, together with a 150 horse power water turbine, gave the mills a total of 1000 horse power. Eight large Lancashire boilers were needed to supply all the steam. Electric light was fitted up in the principle rooms by 1890 and gas required by the company was made on-site. In 1896 it was decided that the mill lighting should be completely electrified and in 1897 an electric railway was installed between Culter railway station and the mill, principally to convey some 5,000 tons of esparto grass bales per year. This was cer-

tainly *'state-of-the-art'* investment. A workforce of over 300, both male and female, were employed on a 35 acre site, most living *"in commodious dwellings"* erected by the Company on their property. The Culter Paper Mills were, therefore, an industrial colony several miles away from the rest of Aberdeen's larger industries.

Stoneywood Mills

During their tour of *"the various large and splendidly equipped departments"* members of the Aberdeen Mechanical Society were shown the complete process of making and finishing at Aberdeen's largest mill, in fact one of Scotland's largest, that of Alexander Pirie & Sons, Stoneywood Works at Bucksburn.

Stoneywood Mill was founded in 1770 and passed by inheritance to Alexander Pirie in 1796. Pirie installed its first Fourdrinier machine in 1820 but nine years later the entire mill was swept away in a flood, some of the workmen on the island being rescued by the coastguard lifesaving apparatus. By 1850 the rebuilt mill employed 200 men, women and boys and by 1890, over 1500. A further 400 women were employed by the firm at the Woodside Mills and over 800 hands at the Union Works and warehouse in Aberdeen

The Stoneywood Mill of Alexander Pirie & Sons Ltd. Courtesy, Aberdeen City Libraries.

where more that 13,000,000 envelopes were made weekly. This envelope production was said to approach one-third of the total made in Britain. By 1907, the Stoneywood mill had 6 papermaking machines, capable of producing almost 200 tons per week of superfine writing and printing paper, cartridge, ledger, best blotting and other papers. Foreign branches in Paris, Johannesburg, New York, Melbourne and elsewhere supported a large staff of overseas travellers who accounted for almost thirty percent of sales.

The Stoneywood mill used all the common papermaking raw materials: linen and cotton rags, esparto grass and woodpulp. The main element in paper is vegetable fibrous matter, but the finished product bears little resemblance to the raw material. Though linen and cotton rags have long been recognised as particularly suitable for good quality paper, at the beginning of the nineteenth century when supplies of rags were low because of the Napoleonic campaign, attempts were made to produce paper from straw. This paper was quite successful but the method turned out to be expensive in chemicals. More suitable as a raw material was found to be the esparto grass that grew in Southern Spain and Northern Africa. By mid-century, when chemical prices had fallen considerably, Britain more than any other country took advan-

tage of this grass. Imports into Scotland reached some 125,000 tons annually by 1907.

After the huge bales of esparto grass had been broken open, their contents were initially cleaned of weeds, de-rooted and so on before being passed to the *'willowing'* machine that beat out much of the dust and sand. An overhead conveyor transported the grass to the boilers, devices sometimes looking a bit like a cross between a pressure cooker and a large concrete mixer, typically capable of holding a load of 2 tons. There, in the presence of caustic soda and steam at a pressure of 50 p.s.i., the grass was softened and broken down for several hours, producing *'half-stuff'*. This treatment was similar to that given to shredded rags, except that for the rags a weaker mixture of soda solution and a lower steam pressure in a smaller boiler were satisfactory.

The fibres of the half-stuff were bleached and reduced in the *'breakers'*, followed by

The Union Works of Alexander Pirie & Sons Ltd., near Joint Station. Courtesy, Aberdeen City Libraries.

General view of the Stoneywood Mill in 1907. The detached building at the top left was the workmen's dining room, still conspicuous today near the main entrance.

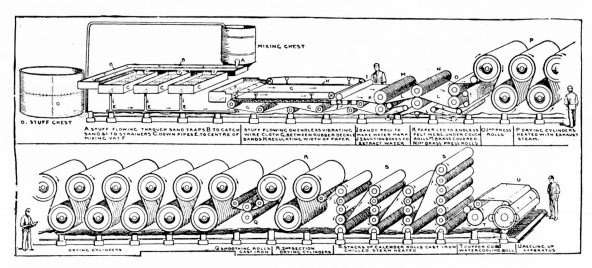

Anatomy of a papermaking machine, 1907.

mincing in the *'beaters'*, troughs containing both fixed and rapidly revolving steel blades not unlike those in a mowing machine. Although this sounds like crude treatment, it was the most delicate operation in that the quality, strength and thickness of the paper depended on judging correctly the length of time in the beaters. It could be between half an hour and twelve hours, depending on the mix of half-stuff and the paper intended.

The paper was finally turned into *'whole-stuff'*, ready for the papermaking machine after appropriate dilution and further filtering. The papermaking machine was enormous, taking in the whole-stuff at the wet end and spreading it over an endless woven wire gauze belt that was shaken sideways to settle the fibres. The formative sheeting was sucked, squeezed, heated and polished to remove excess water, dry it out and smooth it, the tension and pressure in every roller being finely tuned to keep the paper neither over-

stretched nor crinkled. At the dry end of the machine it was finally rolled around a steel bar.

Paper to be used for writing or printing was *'sized'* by coating it so that it did not absorb water so quickly. For *'engine-sized'* paper, a mixture of rosin and alum was added to the pulp in the beaters. *'Tub-sized'* papers were given a superior finish by being passed through gelatine and alum prepared in the mill, and then over open cylinders revolving in hot air produced by steam pipes beneath the driers. The very highest quality paper such as was used for lithographing Ordnance Survey maps was passed sheet by sheet through the gelatine and hung up to dry in a loft.

Most paper was cut to the required dimensions by machine after being passed through a final set of rollers to give the surface texture required. In the overhauling room, girls went over it all sheet by sheet removing blemished material. In other rooms it was machine ruled, if necessary, and packed. So important was the finishing process to the high quality paper Messrs. Pirie marketed, that around the year 1900 a four-storey Finishing House 300 feet long and 240 feet wide was installed at a cost of more than £32,000.

It will be gathered from all this that a large paper works included a vast amount of plant. By 1890 at Stoneywood there were 17 boilers and over 30 steam engines of various kinds. The weekly coal consumption exceeded 500 tons, for it required some 4 tons of coal to produce 1 ton of paper. Little wonder that the site was then dominated by three towering chimney stacks, which rose to heights of 208, 203 and 140 feet respectively.

Stoneywood Mill, 1907: looking down the wet end of a papermaking machine.

By 1907 there were 21 steam boilers in all, some for the papermaking process and some for steam engines. Beneath the chimney stacks 5 large economisers preheated the water for the boilers to 260 degrees Fahrenheit (127 degrees Celsius). The economisers in their turn took water from a hot-well at about 180 degrees Fahrenheit (82 degrees Celsius) that was fed by wet steam which had been used in the drying and heating processes throughout the mill. Among the engines were four large marine-type condensing engines of 500 horse power each and a steam turbo-alternator generating 0.5 megawatts of electricity at 500 volts 3-phase AC, controlled by a Parsons automatic voltage regulator. This was an advanced facility at the time. Electric lighting was powered by a separate 100 kW 220 volt DC dynamo, and supplementary gas lighting was supplied by the works' own gas plant.

Stoneywood also had an exceptional amount of water power, about 1000 horse power mainly provided by three Hercules water turbines installed in the 1880s. Mention has already been made of the firm's Woodside Mill. This was not used for papermaking but for the labour intensive preparation of rags that were stored, sorted, cleaned and cut up by women. There was at Woodside a great water wheel, 21 feet long, about 20 feet in diameter and weighing 50 tons in all. It was built in 1826 and taken out of use in 1965. Wiggins Teape Group, by then the owners of Alexander Pirie & Sons, offered the wheel to the Royal Scottish Museum in Edinburgh. It was dismantled, renovated, chemically treated and re-erected on specially made piers above a suitably large water tank. It can now be seen in the Chambers Street premises of the Royal Museum of Scotland.

The water to power a wheel or turbine can be murky and silty, for it is only the brute force of the water that is required. For the chemistry of papermaking itself, some 300 tons of water were needed for each ton of paper, and it had to be clean water. Stoneywood Mill had a large sedimentation basin of about 15,000,000 gallons containing sand-filters covering an area of 48,000 square feet. The water was pre-treated with lime and

Stoneywood Mill: the drying room for tub-sized paper.

Stoneywood Mill: the plate rolling room in the finishing department.

Stoneywood Mill: hanging hand-sized paper in the drying loft.

Stoneywood Mill; a row of Lancashire type boilers in the boiler room.

aluminium sulphate and, after seeping through the filter, even dirty flood waters were made clear and colourless. About one and three-quarter million gallons a day could be drawn off.

The mill also had a problem in disposing of the contaminated water, particularly the water used to boil the esparto grass and rags. A triple distillation apparatus was used as part of a soda recovery plant that separated the dissolved chemicals and the water in the spent 'soda-lye' from the boiling process. The recovery plant significantly reduced the need for raw chemicals. A completely separate reservoir about a mile away and 150 feet above the mill was maintained to provide a high-pressure water source in case of fire. This system

The Woodside mill, used for rag preparation. Courtesy, Aberdeen City Libraries.

was supplemented by one of Merryweather's steam fire-engines.

Mr. A. G. Pirie, chairman of the company and Honorary Member of the Aberdeen Mechanical Society, was particularly interested in mechanics and steam power. His steam yacht *"Rionnag-na-mara"*, built in 1886 by Rankine & Blackmore, was powered by one of the first really high pressure steam engines built for marine work, quadruple expansion being used. Earlier in the century he had brought over from America what was said to be the first Corliss valve engine ever worked in Great Britain. In 1890 an encomium on the works boasted *"much of the machinery has been devised and perfected by Messrs. Pirie themselves who have always been noted as successful experimentalists and inventors of new methods, new processes, and new means of carrying out the same"*. During the Aberdeen Mechanical Society's visit of 1903 *"members were much struck with the fine machines, the large and clean workrooms, and the scrupulous care exercised in the manufacture of all papers"*. There is little doubt that the firm's prosperity was closely linked with the attention given to the mechanism of papermaking. A. G. Pirie himself died not long after this visit.

Thomas Tait & Sons, Inverurie Paper Mills

Thomas Tait founded the most northerly paper mill in the United Kingdom in 1860, at first using rags only on his one machine. He soon added esparto grass as a raw material but the mill became unusual under the management of his son William when in 1885 they put down a second papermaking machine and associated equipment specially designed to produce papers by their own sulphite process from wood fibres. They were one of the pioneers of using wood pulp and notable as one of the few firms in the country who made their own pulp from raw wood, rather than import it.

Norwegian spruce was bought from Scandinavia in convenient lengths of about 6 feet (ordered by the cubic fathom!). These lengths were cut in three by a swing-frame circular saw and if they still had bark this was removed by the revolving blades of another machine. Residual knots had all to be taken out by the tedious use of vertical drills raised and lowered by the operator's foot. This particular operation was not completely successful because knots seldom grew straight, and efforts were made later to use alternative means of removing them. The prepared logs were reduced to short fibres by successive use of high speed chopper and disintegrater machines. The wood was then ready for the pulp-boilers.

These boilers used the *'quick-cook'* sulphite method, patented in the 1880s. They were built in a lofty brick tower, lined with acid-resisting lead, that was *"quite a feature of the landscape which may be seen for miles around"*. At about a hundred feet high, the tower is still a feature of the mills, though it has long since ceased to be used for boiling wood pulp. After cooking the pulp in a mixture of sulphurous acid and high pressure steam for hours, a dirty brown pulp was produced that had to be thoroughly washed, bleached and broken down in the usual way before being ready for the papermaking machine. Washing was particularly important to ensure all the acid was removed, otherwise the paper would deteriorate later. Disposing of the waste liquor was another problem.

There were two of James Bertram's papermaking machines in the plant, one 72 inches wide for the normal esparto grass paper and the other 86 inches wide for paper made from a mixture of wood and grass pulp. The second machine was driven by a water wheel 20 feet in diameter, 16 feet broad and developing from 150 to 200 horse power, supplemented by steam power; the first was driven entirely by a tandem compound steam engine. In 1911 the original machine of Thomas Tait was replaced as part of a major reconstruction programme. Our photographs show this new machine in the year of its installation.

Thomas Tait & Sons were known for their tub-sized drawing and writing papers, magazine printing papers, music, wall and duplicating paper. For decades, *"Silver linen"* was their well-known letter-quality product.

Further Papermill Visits

In the first year of visits to local industry, in 1889, C. Davidson & Sons Ltd. invited the Aberdeen Mechanical Society to their mill at Mugiemoss. The Society returned in 1909 for a visit that was reported in the press. Then, as now, the firm specialised in commercial and industrial papers. In those days they made products such as wrapping paper, biscuit and grocery papers, cartridge and ammunition

William Tait, whose innovative mill near Inverurie was one of the pioneers of wood-pulp paper in this country. Courtesy, Sheila Tait.

The dry end of Tait's new papermaking machine by James Bertram in 1911. Courtesy, Tait Paper.

Some of the steam-heated drying rollers in Bertram's papermaking machine at Thomas Tait & Sons, 1911. Courtesy, Tait Paper.

paper, paper bags, sacks and so on, largely from recycled rags, jute bags and waste paper. 154 tons a week were produced. Two steam engines, two water turbines and one bucket wheel that gave a total of 800 horse power were, of course, inspected. A considerable time was also spent in the filter house *"where*

Workforce in a papermill: Thomas Tait & Sons in the late nineteenth century. Courtesy, Sheila Tait.

the Don water of the usual brown, muddy-looking condition is put through revolving sand filters, from which it comes out to all appearance – when looked at in a transparent glass vessel – perfectly pure".

The Gordon's Mills Paper Co. Ltd., at Woodside, had the distinction of occupying the oldest paper mill in the Aberdeen area, though for much of the time the mill had produced goods other than paper. When visited in 1891, not long before the Company folded under that name, it produced 40 tons of writing and printing paper per week. Esparto grass and rags were fed into boilers, one for each material, that supplied 6 breakers and 6 beaters. The final mix of pulp, with size and colouring added to order in the beaters, supplied a large G. Bertram papermaker of 107 inches breadth. The largest of three steam engines that ran the machinery was an impressive sight. From a 16 foot diameter flywheel, eighteen 1¾ inch diameter ropes transmitted the power of a 300 horse power horizontal compound engine running off steam at a pressure of 120 p.s.i.

Though the mill looked well equipped and produced large quantities for export, it succumbed to market pressures. Unlike the Culter Mill though, the business rose again from the ashes, reconstituted as the Donside Mill. After several changes of ownership, it still thrives.

City Flour Mills, and the Northern Co-operative Company's Millbank Premises

The City Flour Mills in Causewayend were visited in 1890, four years after a major reconstruction and refitting with new automatic plant supplied by Henry Simon of Manchester. During its passage through the mill from initial hopper to final sacks, the wheat was conveyed from one machine to another by mechanical means alone. The complete mill was driven by a 90 horse power M'Naught beam engine. Let us follow the wheat after its delivery to the granary.

An elevator conveyed it up to the '*dirty wheat*' bins on the second floor from where it was graded by '*sizers*' and passed on through slowly rotating '*cockle*' cylinders that extracted the unwanted cockle seeds, carrying them away by a spiral conveyor. Next it was on to the '*Eureka Magnetic Separator*', a magnetised iron bar placed over the conveyor belt to attract pieces of iron *"often found among the wheat"*. A leather scraper cleared the bar from time to time. This innovation was introduced not particularly to save citizens losing a tooth as they demolished a crusty loaf made from City Mills flour, but to prevent injury to the valuable steel mill-rollers later in the processing.

Dropping from the separator, the wheat passed through a four-section riddle for removing sand, dust, oats, barley and other objectionable matter. It was thoroughly cleansed by a *"Victor"* brush machine with circular brushes rotating at 500 r.p.m. coupled with a fan that blew light wheat, chaff and residual dust into a collecting room. All this preparation was a far cry from milling flour a hundred years before. The wheat was at last ready for the mill proper and was passed between a pair of Leetham's patent automatic feed rollers. Three sets were used for breaking the wheat and seven for reducing the semolina, middlings, etc. One pair of old millstones were retained for producing wholemeal flour. This was not the end of the matter, for there was yet another array of

Davidson's Mugiemoss Mill, from their letterhead of 1910. Courtesy, Aberdeen University Library.

Newly erected Co-op meal and barley mills at Berryden in 1883. Courtesy, Northern Co-operative Society Ltd. and Aberdeen Art Gallery & Museums, Aberdeen City Arts Department.

machines including 'dressing reels', 'sieve scalpers', 'purifiers' and 'centrifugals' for grading and finishing the flour prior to finally sacking it.

The City Flour Mills were capable of turning out about 700 sacks a week, each sack containing 2 bolls and weighing 280 pounds (giving 8 sacks to the ton). The mills' produce was sold *"throughout the country"*.

Not too far away were the Millbank premises of the Northern Co-operative Company Limited (as they were then called), founded in 1861. In 1880 they had built a large mill on that site, which was visited by the Aberdeen Mechanical Society in 1896. Returning in strength in 1905, a party of over 100 Society members were shown round the mill that produced about 350 sacks of meal per week, including oatmeal. They were also shown over the adjacent buildings, particularly the grocery storehouse and bakery.

The immense bakery, by then working at capacity to satisfy over 20 Co-op branches, used 750 sacks per week for loaf (i.e. loaves of bread) and 130 sacks of flour for small bread. In the new portion of the bakery electrically driven mixing, kneading and rolling machines prepared the dough for morning rolls and light bread. A stamping machine cut out various biscuits and placed them on trays that were carried to the oven by boys. A single forty-foot long travelling oven could take morning rolls and light bread, baking the dough as it passed slowly through and delivering it ready for the sale shops at the far end.

Eight separate ovens handled other work and steam plates were used to fire oatcakes and some soft bread. Great emphasis was placed on cleanliness and the absence of handling during the manufacturing process.

In 1905 the Co-op were experimenting with a form of power plant now uncommon, the gas suction engine. The system was developed during the 1880s as an alternative to the steam engine for getting power out of coal. Its basic principle was that the coal was made to generate gas which drove an efficient internal combustion engine. In the version used by the Co-op, the suction stroke of the engine drew air through a well-banked anthracite fire. The carbon of the incandescent coal reacted with the oxygen in the air to give carbon monoxide gas. The hot gas was used to evaporate water and the resulting steam was also sucked into the fire. If the coal was hot enough, this too reacted to produce more carbon monoxide and also hydrogen. All the emerging gases (known as water gas), including the residual nitrogen in the air and various impurities, were passed through a small purifier filled with coke and flushed with a small quantity of water. The air and gas mixture emerged sufficiently clean and cool that it could be fed directly into the gas engine as fuel.

For the experimental 15 horse power gas suction plant under test, the cost in coal was less than two pence per hour at full load. (Coal cost just over £2 per ton. As part of their trade, the Co-op imported coal directly from Sunderland using its own 600 ton steamship). The equivalent electrical power of 11 kilowatt-hours brought from the Corporation supply was more than 5 times the cost. The engine was used to run boring, morticing,

New technology in the early 1900s. A 50 horsepower motor at the Co-op's Berryden Works. Courtesy, North East of Scotland Museums Service.

Steam engine at the Co-op Berryden site, circa 1905. Courtesy, Northern Co-operative Society Ltd.

planing and sawing machinery in the Joinery Department. Elsewhere on site three conventional steam engines aggregating 175 horse power were in operation. By 1907, the Co-op had installed a 92 horse power gas suction plant by Hornsby & Sons for generating its own electricity to light the Millbank premises and power machinery in the bakery.

The Co-op's mechanical workshop at Berryden, circa 1905. Courtesy Northern Co-operative Society Ltd.

The grocery warehouse was a six-storey building with a frontage of 180 feet, fitted with electric lifts, electrically driven fruit cleaning machinery and a great cold store with refrigeration plant driven by a 50 horse power motor. In the cold store were various rooms for cheese, butter and meat of all descriptions kept at appropriate temperatures between 2 degrees and 10 degrees below freezing. Approximately £1000 worth of goods passed daily through the warehouse, including two-thirds of a ton of tea and 70 two-hundredweight bags of sugar. A fleet of horse-drawn vans, supported by a blacksmiths' and cartwrights' workshop, delivered the goods.

The retail trade receives very little coverage within our pages, for the 'mechanical' aspects of it were slight. Nonetheless, it is clear from this glimpse of the Co-op that the advantages of economy of scale, so well known now through the spread of supermarket chains, were appreciated by the larger businesses even at the beginning of the twentieth-century.

6

Services :
Sewerage, Railway Workshops
and the Oldmill Poorhouse

The Girdleness Outfall Scheme

The nineteenth century brought count-less wonders of technology into the world, but I can think of none that benefited more people, rich and poor alike, everyday of the year to greater effect than the installation of the public sewerage system. Accounts of sanitation conditions in the bigger cities in the first half of the nineteenth century make appalling reading. Water itself, being a precious commodity, was used and re-used in the home for increasingly dirty household duties before it was reduced to a filthy black liquor fit to be thrown out into the only drain available, often the street gutter. Cesspools did little more than delay the soakaway of sewage into the water source tapped by the local pump. A continuing population of seriously ill adults and children, dying with diarrhoea, typhus or other fevers, discharged contaminated excreta into the system, maintaining the level of disease. Cholera outbreaks flared up in proportion to the inadequacy of the sewers.

This state of affairs was perpetuated not by wilful neglect but by ignorance of the importance of clean water and adequate sewage disposal. The prevailing opinion until after the middle of the century was that disease was spread by foul air, not filthy water, and that it was scarcely avoidable. There was, indeed, a prodigious stink in many houses,

Crown Street disrupted to take the new sewer, 1901. The rails are for the steam crane. Courtesy, Grampian Regional Council, Department of Water Services.

not only those of the overcrowded poor without any drainage at all. Nonetheless, it took a long time before enough evidence accumulated to force the unwilling ratepayer to spend money cleansing the town. One must remember that it was not until 1860 that Pasteur showed the nature of putrefaction and a few years later that Lister began to show the connection between dirt and sepsis. Some understanding of the bacterial contribution to human disease did not come until the 1870s. Major undertakings to provide Aberdeen with a good supply of clean water fall outside the 25 year period covered by this account. For example, by 1886 there was in place, thanks to developments over the previous 25 years, capacity to take 8 million gallons of water per day from the River Dee, with several large reservoirs in the vicinity of the city providing a total storage capacity of 30 million gallons.

In respect of sewerage, there was nothing backward in Aberdeen's position that the only means of disposing of sewage prior to 1860 consisted of a few very large sewers and several open burns. In the 1860s, a main sewer was built from Aberdeen's western extent at Holburn Street running via the Schoolhill viaduct and Loch Street to discharge its contents onto an irrigation farm of about 45 acres near the Old Town Links. Several branches joined this main pipe. Another sewer discharged into the harbour at Abercromby's Jetty. The sewerage system was expanded on an ad hoc basis but, as the century wore to a close, the growth of the city necessitated a complete review of sewerage provision, preparatory to a major new installation. William Dyack, the Burgh Surveyor, undertook the review in 1894 - 1896 and in the following two years drew up a scheme covering the requirements of the whole expanded city. The Town Council were given the necessary implementation powers under *"The Aberdeen Corporation Act, 1899"* and, with the legislation and planning complete, work began in 1900 on the centrepiece of the plan – the Girdleness outfall sewer.

This sewer was designed to discharge up to 81 million gallons per day, or a quantity equal to 300 gallons per day per person for an estimated population of 270,000, six times the daily dry-weather average flow. This represented far-sighted planning for the future. The new sewer was to be a little over three miles in length. The first section followed a line from Skene Street, deep under Golden Square, down Crown Street and along North Esplanade to its terminus at Point Law. Its construction took from July 1900 to January 1902. The second section, from the Torry side of the River Dee to the North foreshore of Nigg Bay and thence out to sea at Girdleness, was begun in 1902. The two sections were linked by a tunnel under the Dee.

The first section required substantial care because it crossed a busy and well established part of the town. Its building involved total disruption of some streets, for it was sunk in a trench that reached a considerable depth in places. The addition of the electrical subway in the same trench by the contractor Peter Tawse has already been described in chapter 3. It may well be due to Peter Tawse that we owe the existence of excellent photographs of the whole scheme. At one Aberdeen Mechanical Society meeting "*he impressed on young men in particular the value of photography in connection with his own industry in illustrating the progress of work in various stages*". He was an Honorary Member of the Society and was elected Honorary Vice-President from 1905 - 07. He died suddenly early in 1907 while still in office but his contracting business was carried on by his son, William Tawse.

The second section and the Dee tunnel provided a greater technical challenge, met by the resident engineer in charge of the oper-

G.R. Graham Conway, Resident Engineer, 1906. Courtesy, Aberdeen City Libraries.

ation, G. R. Graham Conway, also an Honorary Member of the Aberdeen Mechanical Society. From the Torry valve house beside the Dee, the sewer continued to Sinclair Road and along Greyhope Road to the corner of St. Fittick's Road. It varied in depth from 12 to 28 feet below the surface. Thereafter a tunnel had to be made from three sinking shafts, the deepest of these near Balnagask Road penetrating 100 feet into St. Fittick's Hill. In August 1902, a party of 80 members of the Aberdeen Mechanical Society descended in groups in the shaft cage, to inspect the working face of the tunnel. The track of the tunnel consisted of two straight sections joined by a long bend. In between the first two shafts it ran through boulder clay but in the second section it was bored through hard but fragile granitic rocks that were liable to cave in unless supported extensively.

Down among the woodwork in the sewer trench below street level, 1901. Courtesy, Grampian Regional Council, Department of Water Services.

The tunnel itself was some 10 feet in diameter but after lining the walls with at least 15 inches thickness of brick and concrete the finished sewer had an internal diameter of 7½ feet. This is still more than enough height to stand up in or, more appropriately, paddle a small tub along for inspection. The lower half was lined with red facing brick from the Seaton Brick Works, located just north of Aberdeen. The diameter of 7½ feet was calculated to allow the full capacity of the system to flow at a gradient of 1 in 2000. Where the sewer was comparatively easy to construct, such as when it crossed the agricultural ground of gravel, sand and clay after it emerged from the tunnel, it was reduced in diameter to 5¾ feet. This was a cost saving exercise that recognised it would be many years before the full capacity was needed. It was argued that, when necessary, a duplicate pipe could be constructed alongside the narrow section quite cheaply but that later generations would not want the expense of tunnelling through rock again merely through want of foresight when laying the sewer initially. Rock was again reached near the Nigg foreshore and the full dimensions of the pipe were resumed. The accompanying pictures show very clearly the scale of the enterprise, in which 40,000 tons of gneiss were removed to lay the pipe along this stretch.

At mean tide level there was a penstock and valve house (neatly made in granite) with automatic tidal flap valve that prevented the sea backing up the sewer but opened immediately the pressure of sewage exceeded the pressure of sea on the valve. If required, the sea water could be allowed into the sewer to flush it out. From this valve house the sea outlet took the sewage in a 7 foot internal diameter cast-iron pipe extending 190 yards beyond the low-water mark and 21 feet below high water spring tide. The pipe was brought in sections, each weighing about 7 tons, as can be seen in the illustration. It was covered in a heavy mass of concrete, dovetailed into the rocks.

Taking a rest from lining a narrow section of St Fittick's tunnel by candlelight, circa 1902. Courtesy, Grampian Regional Council, Department of Water Services.

The whole Girdleness outfall scheme was very well engineered by Conway and built to a high standard by Tawse. Although it has been described above in the past tense, every bit of it is still there, in good repair and still in use. The old works form part of the Town's enlarged sewerage system that leads to a new outfall at Girdleness. This takes the sewage in a tunnel two and a half kilometres through the rock below the sea before diffusing it onto the sea bed.

The most difficult section of the original project was the tunnel under the Dee which, with the shafts on either bank, effectively formed an inverted siphon for the sewage. Naturally the shafts were sunk first, each 13 feet in diameter, lined with cast-iron segmented rings and made watertight. The Point Law shaft drops 53 feet and the Torry shaft 62½ feet below the level of high water spring tides. The backbone of the tunnel can be seen in the photograph, taken during construction, to be made of cast-iron rings. They were 8½ feet in external diameter, 18 inches long and weighed one and a third tons. Each ring was built of 5 segments and a key piece, the whole construction of 114 yards in length being bolted together with caulking and over 10,000 one inch steel bolts. The usual rate of progress was two rings, or 3 feet in length, per day. This was achieved by men working three 8-hour shifts per day with a half-hour break between shifts.

The cutting edge of the tunnelling operation was the "Greathead" hydraulic shield with its 18 steel knives around the periphery. Six hydraulic rams pushed the shield slowly forward through the ground, the rams pressing against the last iron ring. The men dug within the shield. A thin layer of Portland cement grout was laid under pressure on the very outside, to protect the iron lining. The technique was very similar to the one employed in the London underground railway borings.

The procedure was not particularly easy because the strata through which the tunnel passed was very loamy alluvial clay 20-28 feet under the river bed, with thin layers of stratified sand that changed easily into silty mud when exposed to ordinary atmospheric conditions. The whole tunnelling operation had to be performed under air at twice atmospheric pressure, supplied by two steam driven compressors each capable of 37,800 cubic feet per hour. All workers (and sight-seeing par-

The Girdleness outfall sewer near the lighthouse. Note the horse-drawn railway sledge on the left bringing bricks and building materials. Courtesy, Grampian Regional Council, Department of Water Services.

ties such as the Aberdeen Mechanical Society) were sealed into an airlock 6 feet high *"until the atmosphere was slowly brought up to the same pressure as that in the tunnel, when a door at the foot was opened, and the descent into the tunnel itself made"*. As a pre-

caution against decompression illness (the 'bends'), a medical airlock was fitted up, but never needed. Long materials such as rails could be passed through a separate airlock in the form of a long tube. Telephone communication linked the tunnel with the airlock and the compressor house, and electric light was used throughout.

Down the centre of the segmented shell of the tunnel an upright steel partition was built of steel plates $5/8$ inches thick to divide the tunnel into two parts, forming duplicate siphons. The whole of the inside was lined with concrete to present a smooth surface to the flow of sewage. At the Torry side, a sludge pit and electric pumping plant was installed so that either siphon could be emptied and cleaned.

With the finishing of the Dee tunnel, the Girdleness outfall scheme was complete. It had cost almost £200,000. The account above has been given in some detail, not only because it was a significant civic undertaking but because it is all too easy to neglect the effort and expense of bringing adequate sewerage to a town. Of course there was more

The Girdleness outfall sewer being led through a solid rock cutting. Courtesy, Grampian Regional Council, Department of Water Services.

Bringing in one of the 7 foot diameter cast-iron sections of the terminating outfall pipe. Courtesy, Grampian Regional Council, Department of Water Services.

Workers 24 feet under the bed of the River Dee at twice atmospheric pressure in the Dee tunnel, 1905. The front section is the Greathead hydraulic shield that can be moved forward. The rear is the metal tunnel shell that was gradually built up behind the shield. Courtesy, Aberdeen City Libraries.

to the development of sanitary engineering than simply the provision of large sewers. Towards the end of the nineteenth century great efforts were made to evaluate the best methods of connecting basins and toilets to sewers, with appropriate water traps; of flushing efficiently and of ventilating drains safely. When every tenement dweller in Aberdeen could pull the chain on the cast-iron siphon cistern above a Victorian pottery water closet, whether in a shared facility on the landing or in an outhouse, a revolution in public hygiene had been effected that was much greater than any subsequent development of bathroom/ toilets with fitted carpet and matching fittings.

The penstock and valve house overlooking Nigg Bay, 1905. Courtesy, Grampian Regional Council, Department of Water Services.

The segmented shell of the sewerage tunnel under the River Dee being divided into two halves prior to lining with concrete, 1906. Courtesy, Grampian Regional Council, Department of Water Services.

Bedding-in the cast-iron outfall pipe to the foreshore rock. Courtesy, Grampian Regional Council, Department of Water Services.

Granite houses over the sewerage shafts at either end of the River Dee tunnel. Foreground, Torry house; background, Point Law house, 1908. Courtesy Grampian Regional Council, Department of Water Services.

Great North Of Scotland Railway Workshops

In April 1850, the first scheduled train to Aberdeen swung over the new river Dee railway bridge and steamed to a halt at Ferryhill station. The Aberdeen Railway Company had effected a breakthrough that was to change the travelling and commercial habits of the town in the space of a few years. Ferryhill was the end of the line, but plans were already afoot to provide railway transport north of Aberdeen under the auspices of a new company, the Great North of Scotland Railway Company (the GNSR). After a succession of delays, the first section of line was at last opened in September 1854, thirty-nine and a half miles from Kittybrewster to Huntly, single track width with occasional crossing places. It was hardly a "*great*" railway in size, but the carriages were considered good, the ride smooth and there was no second-class rolling stock. It was also said to be the only railway in Britain to be opened with electric telegraph throughout its whole length.

From this small beginning, the Great North expanded to a system 287 miles in length, covering Aberdeenshire, Banffshire and Morayshire. It was *the* local railway of North-East Scotland, providing a highway for the flow of products between rural communities and the region's natural gateway, Aberdeen. Various branches had been incorporated as independent lines but most of

The first train from Aberdeen leaves Ferryhill station in April 1850. Courtesy, Aberdeen University Library.

Before the prosperity of the steam trawler age expanded Torry along the shores of the Dee, southbound trains reached countryside across the railway bridge. Note how the clean and solid lines of the granite clad arches were then shown to advantage. Courtesy, Aberdeen University Library, GWW collection no. E2108.

them were consolidated in 1866. A year later, the connection to the south with the Scottish North Eastern Railway (as the Aberdeen Railway had become) was made upon completion of the link down the Denburn and the building of the Joint Station at Guild Street. (The Aberdeen Railway had extended their line to Guild Street in 1854). The Deeside Railway that had been running since 1853 was added to the Company in 1876, and the Morayshire Railway in 1880.

The Great North had vicissitudes of fortune but historians have judged that towards the end of the century it was *"easily the best of all the smaller British Railways"*. During that time the Company was chaired by William Ferguson of Kinmundy. Ferguson was born in the early 1820s, appointed a director of the GNSR in 1867 and chairman in 1879. He was highly respected by the employees. He was also knowledgeable in many branches of science and from 1898 until 1902 was an active Honorary President of the Aberdeen Mechanical Society, chairing meetings and contributing to the expansion of the Society. There was, therefore, a strong interest from the very top of the Board of Directors in the mechanics of keeping the GNSR going.

In the 1890s, the main workshop of the Great North of Scotland Railway at Kittybrewster was a substantial engineering site, building carriages and waggons and carrying out all repairs and replacements to engines, no matter how large. A press report of 1890 described what the Aberdeen Mechanical Society saw as they went round.

The *"running sheds"* provided accommodation for over 60 large engines. One in particular was much admired, *"having a tank capacity of over 3000 gallons, sufficient to enable a train being taken from Aberdeen to Elgin without having to stop for a supply of water"*. Aberdeen to Elgin was 81 or 87 miles, depending on the route; the slow train took over 4 hours and the fast one about half this time. This glimpse of practicalities shows that the nineteenth-century railway engineers had to work very hard to achieve all they did. An *"accident train"* was kept in readiness containing *"all the appliances and tools that thought and experience have suggested as likely to be required in all kinds of accidents"*. These included a crane, jacks, crowbars, hammers and so on, as expected, and also *"a large cooking stove at one end of the van, and provisions in shelves sufficient to supply a*

William Ferguson of Kinmundy, chairman of the GNSR. Courtesy, Aberdeen University Library.

William Pickersgill, GNSR locomotive superintendent. Courtesy, Aberdeen University Library.

GNSR Pickersgill 4-4-0 engine no. 29, built at Inverurie locomotive works in 1909. Copyright Ian Allen Holdings, with permission.

large squad of workmen". There was, in addition, an ambulance and medicine chest for injured passengers. Accident recovery by train was the fastest means available.

The shed where carriages and waggons were built was well equipped with power saws and power planing, moulding, mortising, tenoning and drilling machines; just the equipment of a modern joiners' shop. The carriages went on to the paint shop, where the making and fitting of upholstery was also carried out. In the paint shop *"some very artistic specimens of carriage embellishment were exhibited"*, a comment that serves only to remind us that one hundred years later we travel in the uniformity of mass produced rolling stock.

In 1894 the GNSR appointed the energetic and scholarly William Pickersgill as locomotive superintendent at Kittybrewster. He was only 33 years old but proved his worth by designing the first corridor coaches in Scotland, built in 1896. They were 36 feet long, included lavatories, and were lit by electricity generated by a battery and dynamo driven from the wheels of each coach. First-class coaches had four compartments and third-class, five. It was said they were *"the envy of many other railway companies"*. While at Kittybrewster in the 1890s, Pickersgill also designed a number of GNSR's 4-4-0 locomotives that came to bear his name. This size was the smallest in use for pulling passenger trains but was widely employed by many railway companies. Pickersgill was an Honorary Vice-President of the Aberdeen Mechanical Society from 1900 - 02 and Honorary President from 1902 - 04. In addition, he contributed talks on his own interests during the 20 years he was associated with the Society. He was, for a time, on the Council of the Aberdeen Association of Civil Engineers.

Returning to our survey of the Kittybrewster works, metalwork occupied a

The Inverurie locomotive works boiler and erecting shop, almost 100 yards square. Courtesy, Aberdeen University Library, GWW collection no. F5489.

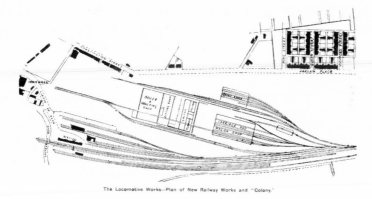

The Locomotive Works—Plan of New Railway Works and "Colony."

Relative location of Inverurie station, the locomotive works and the GNSR housing scheme. Courtesy, Aberdeen University Library.

greater area than woodwork in the complex. 25 forges and two powerful steam hammers were among the equipment in the blacksmiths' shop. The tinsmiths' shop was a large facility with punching, angle-bending, rolling, circle-cutting, moulding, beading and other machinery that allowed the GNSR to be self sufficient in the art of soldered metalwork. Here was made and repaired engine, carriage and permanent way lamps, foot-warmers, oil cans, etc. The machine and fitting shops were *"commodious"* with *"a large and very superior collection of engineers' tools and machines"* that allowed all engine and

maintenance work, boiler rebuilding and so forth to be undertaken. As one example of the work done, it is interesting to note that they made the cars and trailers for the Cruden Bay electric tramway that connected the station to the newly-built Cruden Bay Hotel and 18-hole golf course, all owned by the GNSR. (An excellent picture of the hotel with a tram standing before it is contained in *"50 Views of the Granite City"* published by Aberdeen Journals in 1901).

All this was substantial enough to elicit two further visits from the Aberdeen Mechanical Society in the 1890s and several talks on railway technology during their winter sessions. Nonetheless, during the 1890s Kittybrewster was considered inadequately small and out-of-date by the GNSR. Maintenance and renewal of rolling stock was one of the heaviest items of railway expenditure, the cost of repairs alone to locomotives averaging 25 to 30 percent of their working expenses. Any economies and improvements in this field resulting from a well-run modern workshop would show dividends in an improved service to customers. With this in mind, the GNSR acquired a site of about 25 acres, half a mile north of (the old) Inverurie station. A completely new station, commended for its

The 60 ton lift travelling electric crane in the erecting shop preparing to hoist a locomotive. Courtesy, Aberdeen Art Gallery & Museums, Aberdeen City Arts Department, and the GNSR Association.

The powerhouse of the Inverurie locomotive works, Pickersgill's two 100 horse power steam engines driving DC dynamos. Courtesy, North East of Scotland Museum Services.

elegance, was built with its main entrance facing the square, and opened with much colour and spectacle on the snowy winter's day of 10th February 1902. Adjacent were the locomotive, carriage and waggon works erected at a cost of about £100,000. Their construction had been going on since 1898 and one third of the staff of 340 were already at work within. The buildings of grey Tyrebagger granite were spread over four large "shops" and some smaller sheds.

The boiler, erecting and machine shop was almost 100 yards square, subdivided within for the three activities. The erecting shop was capable of accommodating 28 locomotives in various stages of repair and

The Inverurie locomotive works blacksmiths' shop at work. Courtesy, North East of Scotland Museum Services.

construction. Highlight of three visits to the works by the Aberdeen Mechanical Society was a demonstration of the 60 ton travelling electric crane spanning the north bay. It could with ease lift a 40 ton engine over the other engines in the shop and "whisk" it to the spot where work was to be carried out, as shown in the illustration. (In some parts of the shop there were specialised machines for tasks like cylinder boring). This modern facility avoided cutting up the floor space with turntables, traversing lines and other dead space. It owed it existence to the relatively recent development of the heavy-duty electric motor whose power-to-weight ratio was much better than the engine in a steam crane. Five such motors drove the different movements of this crane.

On the advice of William Pickersgill, electric equipment was a key feature of the new works. 200-candle-power arc lamps lit all the shops except the paint shop, which was lit by 240 incandescent lamps of 16-candle-power. The carriage and waggon shop had almost 400 of these incandescent lamps in addition to its arc lamps. Electricity drove many of the machines, including a 50 horse power blower for the 36 fires in the smithy. Two 100 horse power compound steam engines coupled to electric dynamos provided most of the electric current for the works at 220 volts DC, with a smaller dynamo charging a bank of storage cells. Four locomotive-type boilers generated the steam required not only for the dynamos' engines but also for three steam hammers in the smithy, a compressor for the pneumatic mains supply and steam heating pipes in the paint shop.

Water was provided from a special supply secured by the GNSR by impounding the Polinar Burn some two and a half miles away and constructing a reservoir. The pipes from the reservoir were duplicated, one set being kept for use in case of fire. This eventuality could be handled by the works' own Fire Brigade "thoroughly organised and equipped" with a hose cart and portable steam-driven pumping gear capable of throwing 300 gallons per minute to a height of 150 feet. A 50,000 gallon tank on the roof of the boiler house held a reserve supply for the works. Drinking water came independently from the Inverurie domestic supply.

By 1907, the Company claimed that "the population of Inverurie has, since these Works were opened, increased by about

1,200". They had built seven blocks of houses, each with accommodation for 16 families, fitted out with modern appliances and electric light taking current from the railway works. (Electric light in domestic houses was not at all common when it was installed in 1902). Some larger houses were also built for the foreman and senior staff. The Company provided land for use as garden plots, a recreation hall including reading and billiard rooms, and technical evening classes during the winter session. The Works had Dramatic, Musical and Ambulance Societies.

In truth, an undertaking that was planned in a buoyant period for the GNSR proved a bit large for the company when business failed to grow as expected once the twentieth century got underway. Not greatly deterred, they used surplus capacity to build bodies for motor buses and char-a-bancs that were run by the Company as a connecting service or as a tourist attraction linked with the trains.

What distinguishes a twentieth century factory from its nineteenth century counterpart is not usually the principles of the machinery employed (at least not until the age of computer control) but the attention given to organisation of detail so as to maximise the use of resources. It was this careful planning that enabled manufacturers to produce complicated articles of high quality with an enormous saving of time, and consequently at a price that the mass market could afford. The popular motor car that was to appear from the highly organised works of Ford, Morris and Austin illustrates the principle very well. By this standard, the Inverurie loco workshops were a fitting introduction of twentieth century practices to the region. Under the admirable superintendence of William Pickersgill, Patrick M. Barnett (chief engineer, active member of the Aberdeen Mechanical Society and first President of the Aberdeen Association of Civil Engineers), J. F. Drake (chief draughtsman, and President of the Aberdeen Mechanical Society in 1903-04) and other senior Great North men, the works were organised and run with considerable professionalism. They were also, it is clear, run with pride.

The Oldmill Poorhouse

Lying in Woodend Hospital for a few weeks last year, with plenty of time to inspect what little of the architecture could be seen through a few windows, I was quite unaware

1908 drawing of the central block of the Aberdeen Parish poorhouse (now the Glenburn Wing of Woodend Hospital), opened 1907. Courtesy, Aberdeen Journals.

of the purpose for which the buildings had been erected in the first place. Having dealt in this chapter with two such diverse services as the public sewerage and the private railways, it will not be out of place to finish with a visit to another quite different service whose scale merits the description of 'industry' – the Poorhouse at Oldmill, now the nucleus of Woodend Hospital.

When the Aberdeen Parish Council decided to replace their two existing poorhouses at Fonthill and at Nelson Street by a single institution, they planned a substantial complex, with provision in the first instance for 650 inmates, besides the necessary staff. The Council purchased the 55 acre estate of Oldmill upon which stood the Oldmill Reformatory for boys and an arable farm. Plans for the new complex, made public in November 1901, showed that the old Reformatory buildings were to be demolished to make way for a large central building with extensive wings (now the Glenburn Wing at Woodend), detached hospital blocks (now amalgamated as the main hospital block), a special hospital for infectious diseases and a detached nurses home (a modern develop-

ment in those days). When one looks today at the imposing central tower and entrance to the old administrative block, it is an astonishing testament to the standards of 1901 that the Parish Council regarded this as the least ornate option they could erect. *"It is not intended that any expense should be put upon fine masonry details"* they remarked, *"the effect of a satisfactory composition will, therefore, be obtained by means of grouping the various buildings"*. The grouping was designed to present *"a suitable yet dignified appearance"* for passers-by on the Skene Road, a few hundred yards away. Hence the tower, with its four-dial clock costing around £130.

A notable feature of the central block was its large hall, where inmates met for meals, evening and Sunday worship, and for such communal entertainment as was arranged. Adjacent was the large kitchen in which all cooking was done by steam, with special appliances for cooking soups, potatoes and fish. Considerable emphasis was laid on self-sufficiency for the premises. Near the central block was the laundry, washhouse, drying-loft and the *"stick house"*

Within the main hall of the poorhouse. Courtesy, Grampian Health Board Archives.

where male inmates were given light employment such as breaking and bundling firewood, tailoring and cobbling to make their own clothes and shoes, and painting.

In the grounds there was plenty of room for growing all their own potatoes and other market-garden produce. In addition, they had *"a splendidly equipped dairy and farm steading"*. To improve the appearance of the surroundings, the Parish Council were lucky to be offered by the Wrights & Coopers Incorporation the shrubs and plants belonging to the estate of the late Mr John Fyfe. While in the grounds, mention must also be made of the controversial viaduct built to span the Denburn ravine. The main drive from the Skene Road to the Poorhouse was carried on 9 strong piers of heavy masonry built at a cost of several thousand pounds. It now blends attractively into the landscape, but since that entrance has been closed to regular traffic it is not usually seen by visitors.

The Aberdeen Mechanical Society visited the Poorhouse in strength, along with the Wrights & Coopers, not long before the first inmates were transferred in May 1907. Of course they showed special interest in the mechanical appliances for the production of light, heat, power, ventilation and other amenities. The party was guided through about two miles of underground passages that comprised the heating and ventilation ducts. Electricity was generated on-site by steam engines directly coupled to dynamos giving 200kW for lighting and power. That electricity was not obtained from the Town's new generating station rankled Town Councillor James Taggart a bit while he was proposing a vote of thanks on behalf of the Mechanics. He grudgingly acknowledged that *"as the members of the Parish Council were men of light, he had no doubt that they knew best about the manufacture of it"*.

The Town also regretted the loss of rates incurred by locating the Poorhouse outside the City boundary and, interestingly, the decision not to take the Town's water supply. The Town's water rate of about £500 per annum was considered an unacceptable burden on Poorhouse running costs by the Parish. They set about sinking their own artesian well in the grounds and at the time of the visit had reached a depth of 210 feet and a plentiful supply of water. The superintending engineer, James Stewart, was continuing to 250 feet. The visitors, including Town Councillor Taggart, were offered a drink from the well. It had probably not gone unnoticed that on another occasion Taggart was reported to have said that *"the Parish Council had gone a little too far ... in providing such a magnificent country mansion"* for the poor.

The size of the whole undertaking was substantial, it being aimed at *"the aged and respectable poor, and also for orphan children in the city"*. Provision was made for every age group, from babies in the maternity ward of the hospital and children in a block attached to the female wing of the main building. There was also a detached mortuary and small chapel. The dominance of hospital facilities arose because the Parish was obliged by the Poor Laws to offer relief to its paupers, excluding able-bodied adults. Consequently, the poorhouse medical provisions catered only slightly for accidents and short-term illnesses, and mainly for the long-term care of the chronically sick and incurable. For this purpose (local) rates were levied from all owners and occupiers of property. The resulting administration of the Poor Laws was one of the most important duties of the Parish Council. Criticism of the poorhouse system led, ultimately, to the Social Services and National Health Service with which my generation has grown up. From this brief account of the provision for Aberdeen's new Poorhouse, there is no doubting the sincerity of those who established such institutions. Nonetheless, I for one would prefer to attend Woodend Hospital in the care of the National Health than as a poorhouse inmate.

7

The Diverse Economy

The Local Press

A visit to the local newspaper was an obvious choice of outing for a mechanical society, since the printing press alone was an astonishing piece of mechanism. Many people are familiar with the office copying machine that produces one A4 sheet per second, on a good day; or the home computer printer that manages a few sheets per minute. Now try to imagine a machine which is a maze of cog-wheels, cylinders, rollers, adjusting screws and iron-framing that prints a full width of thin broadsheet newsprint in small type on both sides, cuts it, paginates it and folds it at the rate of 48,000 six-page newspapers per hour. One's first reaction is that it surely cannot be done. Yet, that was the performance of the new Goss patent three-roll straight line machine seen in operation printing and folding copies of the *"Evening Express"* in 1901.

A representative of the Goss Company explained the operation of the machine, which was driven by a 30 horse power electric motor. *"The beautifully finished and brightly kept machine, with its wonderfully rapid but smooth motion, was greatly admired"*, according to a reporter's enthusiastic description of the scene. This performance was, admittedly, at least twice as fast as the three older machines still working then in the offices of *"The Aberdeen Journal"* and *"Evening Express"*. The fastest of these, a Hoe machine driven by a steam engine, was also printing and folding the *"Evening Express"*, at the rate of 24,000 per hour. By 1905, the old machines had been replaced by a second Goss press and in 1911 steam was abandoned for electricity.

Printing was only the final stage in the production process. A visit to the stereotyping department showed the moulding and casting of stereoplates; in the zincography, the making of zinc and copper engravings. The Linotype department was regarded as even more wonderful than the

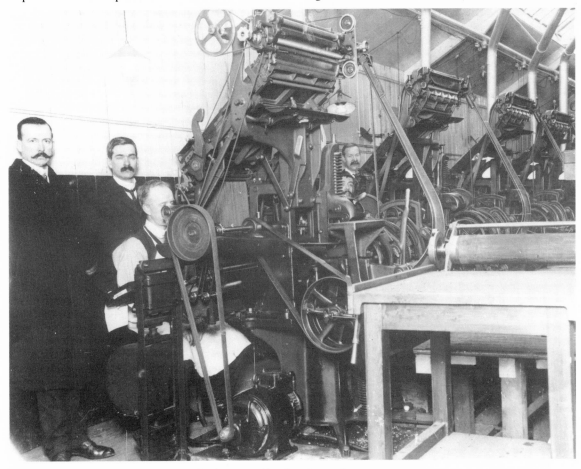

Linotype machines at Aberdeen Journals. Courtesy, Aberdeen Journals.

printing, perhaps because many of the visitors were familiar with the normal foundry practice of casting iron, brass, bronze and similar materials. This could be a time-consuming process. In the Linotype machine (then fairly new technology imported from America), text typed-in assembled a matrix of brass letter moulds. When a complete line had been entered, an ingenious mechanism filled it out to the correct length with spaces, and the whole line of type was *"cast while you watched"* in metal, and then delivered. Hence the name of the machine. The letter moulds were automatically replaced in their correct slots.

The Linotype machine is indeed an impressive piece of mechanism, word processing with a complex of well-oiled levers, cams, slides, rotors, tension springs and adjusting arms. The urgent clattering of a row of these machines in operation is equally arresting. In the 1980s they disappeared like ice on a summer's day with the advent of computerised typesetting. When Linotype machines first appeared, however, a great many hand compositors were put out of work. In fact, it was the combination of Linotype machine and rapid rotary printing using pages cast in half-cylindrical metal form that revolutionised the mechanical production of newspapers over the quarter century we have been surveying.

Other departments in the Broad Street office included the literary staff, artists, the telegraph office, filing office, press room, despatch room, letterpress printing, newspaper stores, joiners' workshop and boiler house. *"The Aberdeen Journal"* is well known as the oldest newspaper in Scotland, having been founded in 1748 by James Chalmers as a weekly enterprise. In 1876 the ownership of *"The Aberdeen Journal"* passed to the Aberdeen & North of Scotland Newspaper & Printing Co. Ltd., who two months later converted it from a weekly to a daily newspaper. In 1879 they founded the *"Evening Express"*. The manager, Mr J. A. C. Coutts was for a long time active in the Aberdeen Mechanical Society and a regular speaker at their annual reunion dinners.

Under *"The Aberdeen Journal"* imprint they also published special works, often of a commemorative nature. At the time of the visit they were printing *"50 Views of the Granite City"* with fine half-tone photogravure pictures *"for which there was a great demand"*. This publication was reissued in 1902 as *"60 Views..."* and in 1903 as *"132 Views..."*. Earlier productions seen were *"A Record of Northern Valour"*, *"A Souvenir of Sympathy"*, *"Concerning Three Northern Newspapers"* and the annual *"Aberdeen Almanac and Northern Register"*. The next issue of the *"Aberdeen Weekly Journal"* was in preparation. There was no press monopoly in the district, for the *"Aberdeen Free Press"* and its *"Evening Gazette"* were still in competition. Their offices had been visited by the Society in 1892.

Many journalists might shudder to think that their copy produced in haste to meet the daily deadline could be scrutinized carefully 50 years, 100 years, or more, later as valuable historical evidence. Nonetheless, this book owes a lot to reports in the *"Journal"* and the *"Free Press"* and to their editorial policy that gave the Aberdeen Mechanical Society a generous allowance of column inches. The two papers amalgamated in 1922, discontinuing the *"Evening Gazette"*.

Albert Sawmills

John Fleming established the Albert Sawmills in 1884 on a 3½ acre site at the Albert Quay, owned by the Harbour Commissioners. They constructed a rail line running from the adjacent timber quay (that was specially built) to within the yard. Up-to-date frame saws, circular saws, moulding and planing machines were installed to prepare wood from its imported state, the machinery being driven by a 100 horse power steam engine supplied by a boiler fed on wood-waste. Their palisade perimeter fence was an unusual sight in Aberdeen. By the early 1890s the yard had 3 frame and 10 circular saws; band, German and other sawing apparatus; 3 flooring and 3 moulding machines and a variety of lathes, morticing, boring and like machinery powered by an additional engine. They had added the nearby Esplanade Yards at the other side of Market Street, fronting the river, to give a further two and a half acres of space, mainly for storage.

To match the growth in house-building in the 1890s, there was a buoyant demand for products like roof timbers, sarking, tongue-and-grooved flooring, finished mouldings and, later, pre-cut plaster laths. Cabinet-makers and joiners used many fancy hardwoods and veneers. Spokes and felloes for cartwrights were a speciality. The prosperous fish trade required herring barrel staves, fish boxes, hardwoods such as teak and mahogany for finishing steam trawlers and more pliable woods for small boat-building enterprises that equipped the inshore line and shell fishermen. There were numerous other users of wood.

After John Fleming & Co. became a limited company in 1890, taking over a rival business, they were by far the largest wood merchants in Aberdeen. The Albert Sawmills were visited by the Aberdeen Mechanical Society in 1892, when some more knowledgeable members remarked *"that the Scotch mills were as a rule better equipped and abreast of the times than they had seen in the sister country [England]"*.

A great fire in 1896 destroyed much of the machinery and stock in the main shed, including the travelling electric crane. The Aberdeen Mechanical Society returned in 1897 to find that the firm had survived the mishap and maintained a high standard of re-equipment. John Fleming himself was by this time a prominent Town Councillor and from 1898 to 1902 he served as Lord Provost. During part of his term he was Honorary President of the Aberdeen Mechanical Society, delivering to them a well-reported lecture on *"The Ethics of Mechanical Engineering"*. During his talk in November 1900 he remarked that *"one of the dreams of his municipal life was to see a school of engineering, mechanical and electrical, started in Marischal College"*. These were early days in a campaign that would last over two decades.

Being Lord Provost did not earn him any favours from the Harbour Commissioners, who increased his rent to a level he considered unwarranted. A determined character of strong personality, he responded by purchasing a 4½ acre site at St. Clements, Footdee, outside the Commissioners' jurisdiction. At considerable expense he moved the whole yard there in 1903 and it must have been due to his influence that the street Martin Avenue beside the new premises was renamed as Baltic Place, to reflect the origin of much of his imported timber. Little re-equipping was entailed in the move but he did purchase in 1902 a second-hand compound steam engine from Alex. Hadden & Sons, woollen manufacturers, which served the firm until the mill machinery was entirely electrified in 1963.

John Fleming was knighted in 1908, for his public services. By then Sir John had relinquished many of these and was able to spend more time managing the business. The Society visited the Baltic Place premises in 1909. At that time they had 2 horizontal saws, 4 frame saws, 4 flooring machines, 5 moulding machines, 6 Casson saw-benches, 7 ordinary saw benches, band saws and fret saws, turning lathes and two separate installations of suction piping for exhausting sawdust and chips. The sawdust was bagged and sold. John Fleming & Co. Ltd. are still prominent North-East timber merchants, with several branches outside Aberdeen.

Seaton Brick & Tile Works, Strabathie

The Strabathie works at the Black Dog were visited in 1901 and 1904 by means of their own light railway that ran about three and a half miles from the Bridge of Don depot. The railway had a 3 foot gauge, and 5 waggons 9 feet by 5 feet that could each take 4 to 5 tons of bricks. Passengers were carried in old tramway cars. Pulled by the twelve-and-a-half ton tank engine *"Newburgh"*, these cars skirted the west side of Balgownie links before crossing the dunes to the works themselves. Many of the 100 employees went daily by this means, though 12 families lived in Company cottages adjacent to the works.

The Strabathie site was developed at the end of the nineteenth century to exploit a 20 acre clay bed at Black Dog Farm near the sea beach. The first bricks were delivered in the spring of 1899. Squads of men were employed extracting the clay from a pit that varied from 12 to 25 feet deep, loading it into small low-wheeled waggons that were hauled by endless chain up a narrow-gauge line to the top of the

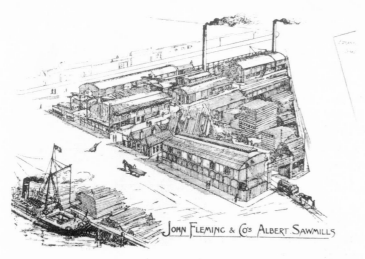

The Albert Sawmills. Courtesy, Aberdeen City Libraries.

Letterhead of the Seaton Brick and Tile Co. Their Head Office pictured is now the Clydesdale Bank, 182 Market Street. Courtesy, Aberdeen University Library.

mill. There it was dropped into the *"tippler"* mill where a series of rollers and mixers crushed and cleared out the stones. The moist clay passed through into the pug mill, something akin to a mincing machine, that homogenized the clay and extruded it through a die using a pressure of 60 to 70 tons per square inch. A series of tightly stretched piano wires divided each block of clay into 10 bricks. Up to 35,000 of these bricks could be produced per working day. For moulded bricks, the material was then taken directly from the brick-making machine to one of 7 brick moulding presses, capable of producing 20,000 bricks per day in aggregate.

Traditional brickworks were labour intensive, it being common in at least one part of the country to employ women for moulding, moving and loading bricks. The Strabathie works were notable because after the bricks were formed, they were not handled again until stacked into the kilns. Cars holding 560 bricks transported them to the tempering chamber at 60 degrees Fahrenheit, where they remained for 12 hours. They next

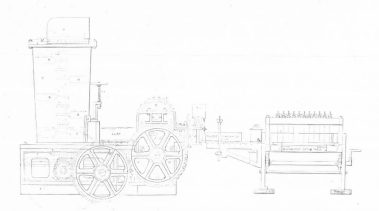

Brick making machine similar to that used at the Strabathie works. Clay is fed into the pug mill on the left and forced out into a rectangular stream which is cut into individual bricks by the stretched wires on the right.

passed to the drying house that consisted of two tunnels each 130 feet in length with accommodation for 90,000 bricks. Below the perforated floor carrying the car rails, 30,000 feet of iron piping were steam heated by a boiler. The rising hot air at approximately 180 degrees Fahrenheit carried the moisture from the bricks. These facilities allowed the works to be kept going all year, regardless of the weather. Finally, the bricks were fired at temperatures up to 2000 degrees Fahrenheit in one of two kilns capable of taking 29,000 bricks between them.

A twin condensing steam engine working to 250 horse power drove the machinery via shafting and belts. Part of the water supply was pumped up by a windmill from a spring on Harehill Farm to a small reservoir. Electric lighting throughout was generated by the Company's own dynamo.

Some, at least, of Seaton's bricks can be recognised by the stamp 'ABERDEEN' impressed on them. In addition to bricks of various grades, the works made drain pipes, roof tiles, wall tiles, chimney pots, flower pots and other earthenware on quite a scale. The Company folded about 1925 and the light railway was taken over by the Murcar Golf Club.

The Aberdeen Steam Laundry Co. Ltd.

The Claremont Street works that were opened in 1888 *"in the opulent west-end suburb of the city"* were specially designed for the business by the Company, who were the pioneers of steam driven laundering in Aberdeen. The laundry itself had begun in 1879. In the early 1890s their wash house was fitted with steam washers, boilers, rinsing vessels, tubs for handwork and hydro extractors. These last items were not mere mangles but may have been an early form of spin drier. The Company were well aware that the machinery of the day could not cater for lighter and more delicate fabrics: *"all the bad features of public steam laundries have been got rid of by the substitution of hand washing for machinery, where necessary"*. By one means or another *"all classes of fabrics can be thoroughly cleaned with even less wear and tear than they would experience at the knuckles or on the washboard of the most careful laundry maid or housewife"*.

Drying and bleaching were undertaken outside when the weather permitted, or in drying rooms fed with hot air. Clothes were ironed by gas iron or mechanical rollers. Car-

The Claremont Works of the Aberdeen Steam Laundry in the early 1890s. Courtesy, Aberdeen City Libraries.

Ironing room in the Aberdeen Steam Laundry, early 1890s. Courtesy, Aberdeen City Libraries.

pets were beaten by a mechanical beater. The fashions of the day dictated that many items should be starched and treated with *"the most improved calendering and polishing machinery, producing a gloss and surface impossible to attain with the hand iron – a great advantage in collar and cuff dressing"*. One can glimpse between these lines the vast amount of drudgery involved in clothes washing and preparation that used to fall upon the servants in more well-to-do households. Mechanical laundering was in its infancy but there is little doubt that almost every housewife in the country has benefited from its subsequent development and spread into our homes.

The Palace Hotel

The Palace Hotel was acquired and reopened by the Great North of Scotland Railway Company in 1891 after a fortune had been spent on making it *"one of the very finest hotels in Europe"*. Indeed, a whole new floor had been added to the Palace Buildings

in a way that still preserved the handsome turreted Union Street facade. The site was one of the best in Aberdeen, commanding a fine prospect of some of the best architecture in the city and located conveniently near Joint Station, to which it was connected by a private covered passage.

Our picture shows the vestibule where the Aberdeen Mechanical Society assembled in 1893 for an inspection of the heating and lighting plant. They were to return there on many occasions for annual reunion dinners. The vestibule was furnished with an inlaid ceramic tile floor, panelled walls decorated with marbles relieved by pilasters and Cornish mouldings, all illuminated through stained glass windows. Further in, we find a coffee-room, drawing and reading rooms *"palatial in their appointments"*, commercial, writing and smoking rooms *"admirably appointed and decorated"*; farther back *"a suite of lavatories exhausting the resources and art of Doulton and Co."*. Up the white polished marble staircase *"a billiard room, very handsomely furnished in gold and leather papers, and lit from a massive dome roof"* was provided with two of Messrs. Burroughs & Watt's best tables. On the third floor, the culinary departments were presided

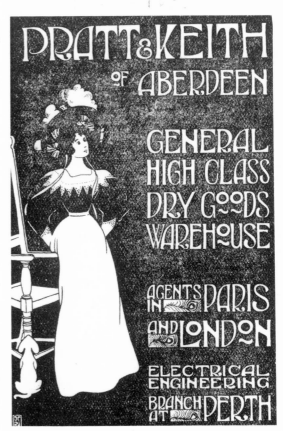

Advertisement for Pratt & Keith, 1905. Courtesy, Aberdeen University Library.

Vestibule of the Palace Hotel, circa 1893. Courtesy, Aberdeen City Libraries.

Advertisement for the Palace Hotel, 1907. Courtesy, Aberdeen City Libraries.

Not Pratt & Keith's emporium but the millinery department of the Co-op, circa 1905. Courtesy, Northern Co-operative Society Ltd.

over by three accomplished French chefs. We are in danger of being distracted from the purpose of the visit.

The Society spent most of their time in the basement, where two separate electric lighting plants of dynamos and accumulators provided power for the 500 lamps of between 8 and 50 candle power that were distributed throughout the hotel. The plants also powered lifts of the latest American manufacture that served passengers and luggage between all floors. Appropriately enough, two large boilers of the locomotive type (not usually seen in stationary installations) provided steam for a pair of engines totalling 140 horse power that drove the dynamos.

The boilers also fed some 2000 feet of steam heated coils that were an integral part of a highly acclaimed heating and ventilation system. This was based on three lines of air ducts which spread throughout the hotel. Blackman fans drew in fresh air through a screen of cocoa-nut fibre cords down which water trickled. The washed air was heated by the coils and forced through the ducts, to be delivered out of a vent above the door in each room. The whole of the air in the hotel was changed not less than four times per hour. It must have been some advantage to guests that they did not have to open their windows to get fresh air, for the noise in such a central location in town, virtually on top of the railway station, was one of the few detractions of the Palace Hotel. Competitors were not slow to try to make something of this real or imaginary disadvantage, for there was little enough else they could be critical of.

Before leaving the Palace Buildings, it is worth looking into the ground floor and lower ground floor that were occupied by Pratt & Keith, one of the largest retail drapery and furnishing businesses in the city. Founded in 1837, they had moved into the buildings in the mid 1870s and expanded to become one of Aberdeen's great emporiums, with a staff of over 200. The furniture stock alone occupied nearly 15,000 square feet. The drapery provided fabrics from linens to silks, velvets and laces *"of every description"*. The many clothes departments ranged from millinery (including flowers, feathers, accessories and trimmings), dinner, evening and reception dresses to the *"famous Aberdeen winseys in white, pink and blue for children's underwear, exported all over the kingdom"*. Aberdeen was noted for many products.

The Palace Buildings were destroyed by fire on 31st October 1941.

The Aberdeen Royal Infirmary

Both ventilation systems and electric plant were topical in 1893. The next visit of the Aberdeen Mechanical Society was to the new electric lighting plant at the Royal Infirmary, briefly mentioned in chapter 3. It was a model installation, built in 1892 at a cost in excess of £8,000. One technical writer commented *"there perhaps is not another boiler, engine, dynamo, and cell-room, with such complete plant, to be found in the north of Scotland"*.

Two boilers of 100 horse power supplied steam at a pressure of 120 p.s.i. for the engines and at a reduced pressure for heating, cooking and laundry work carried on within the infirmary. Initially a pair of horizontal engines each drove a dynamo capable of supplying 240 amps either for working the lighting directly at about 100 volts or for charging a bank of accumulators. A third engine and dynamo was added soon after.

Several miles of insulated cable were laid in specially prepared canary wood grooved casings. In 1892 over 410 lamps were installed, ranging from 8 to 150-candle power according to their position and use. Every bed was fitted with a reading lamp, a portable lamp for examining patients, and with wall attachments so that electro-medical appliances could be plugged in. 16-candle power lamps were used for ordinary lighting throughout the building and 150-candle power lamps for the operating theatres,

Engine house of the Aberdeen Royal Infirmary electric lighting plant, 1892, showing the two horizontal engines by Marshall & Sons of Gainsborough.

engine and boiler rooms. Shirras, Laing & Co. provided the fittings. *"The Aberdeen Journal"* commented *"formerly many of the rooms and passages were extremely dark, but now there is not one which is not amply flooded with light"*.

Boot and Shoe Manufacture

Shoemaking in the nineteenth century was almost completely revolutionised by the advent of powered machinery, so-much-so that industrial shoemakers became a class of skilled machine operators. Each person specialised in making one particular part and no individual turned out a complete pair of shoes. At first, sewing machines outperformed in neatness and speed the best efforts of shoemaker's fingers; later, machines shaped the leather to the foot and curled it around the insole faster than any hand tools. As well as enormously increasing the quantity of footwear in the country, the machinery also led to a general rise in standards for the multitude who could afford only the average products of the trade.

Manufacturers around Aberdeen included the Spey Boot Works, the Co-op Boot and Shoe Workshop and the Ellonbank Boot Factory of William Smith and Sons. These probably represented the largest undertakings but it is difficult to gauge the extent of shoe production in Aberdeen a hundred years ago. In the Aberdeen Directory for 1900, there are 128 entries under *"Boot and Shoe Makers"* but many of these appear to be stores, one suspects with a modest cobbler's workshop attached. Whatever the exact figure, Aberdeen's industries were small in comparison with the country's main shoe factories around Leicester and Nottingham where approximately 50,000 people were employed.

The Spey Boot Works of Mr Lewis Morrison in 62-66 Leadside Road were established in 1899 and when visited in 1900 employed 50 hands. As a new business it was equipped with the latest type of machinery, much of which was made in America, from where a large amount of the hides also originated. Downstairs, the heavier machines were operated by men; upstairs, young ladies managed sewing, cutting, punching, eyeletting and other machines used particularly for preparing and finishing the uppers. The making of a single boot from leather entailed an astonishing number of steps. Numerous different

Inside the Co-op Boot and Shoe Repair Shop, circa 1905. Courtesy, Northern Co-operative Society Ltd.

thicknesses and qualities of leather had to be specially selected, cut, shaped, positioned and put together by machinery using tacks, nails or sewing, as the parts dictated. Leather, being a natural product, always required an experienced eye to get the best out of it. When the boot had been assembled, it had to be trimmed, burnished, coloured, waxed, polished and boxed. By the time a return visit to the Spey Boot Works was arranged in 1910, over 400 different varieties of boot were made there. The works continued in Leadside Road until 1934.

The Ellon Wholesale Boot and Shoe Factory, visited in 1894, 1898 and 1906, was *"beautifully situated behind the railway station"*. It too had American machinery of the latest design, including a *"wonderful piece of mechanism"* for wire-stitching boots. It also

Selling a range of local and national shoes at the Co-op shoe shop, circa 1905. Courtesy, Northern Co-operative Society Ltd.

had its own electric lighting plant, driven from a 30 horse power steam engine, and its own small oil gas plant.

Coachbuilders

With perhaps a little parochial exaggeration it was said in 1890 that the name of R. & J. Shinnie *"is probably as well known as that of any other firm of carriage builders in the whole United Kingdom"*. The firm began in 1870 in Langstane Place and removed to Union Row in 1878 where they expanded to cover an acre of land in a series of detached multistoried brick buildings. The Union Row showroom (100 feet long by 40 feet wide) exhibited *"one of the largest and most varied displays of vehicles of every description found in the north of Scotland"*. During the 1890s they made virtually everything from horse-drawn trams for the Aberdeen Tramway Company down to dainty pony gigs. The standards of workmanship in the shops for wood-working, blacksmiths, body-making, leather working and painting were all high. As a result, R. & J. Shinnie commanded a large home and export trade that gave employment to 170 hands in the early 1890s.

The era of the horse-drawn coach was declining and R. & J. Shinnie changed with the times. When the Aberdeen Mechanical Society revisited the works in 1906, they were conducted round by the next generation of Shinnies, James Jnr. and Patrick Ness Shinnie, himself a member of the Society. *"Various automobile bodies of varied and beautiful design in course of construction for the show to be held in the Olympia, London, in November were first examined, and admiration of the workmanship was freely expressed"*. Three hundred hands were employed by then and the firm were agents for Delaunay-Belleville cars. If there had been a local engineering firm able to produce engines to match Shinnie's coachwork, subsequent Motor Shows might have seen Aberdeen's own car and the town could have boasted a car plant. By 1906, however, the coach business was by no means dead and Shinnie's continued to make, sell and hire a wide range of carriages including landaus, broughams, waggonettes, Whitechapel and rustic carts. R. & J. Shinnie remained in Union Row until 1926 when the premises passed to Aberdeen Motors and other users. Patrick Shinnie moved to College Street under his own name, specialising in Morris cars. Patrick N. Shinnie

Ltd. continued there until about 1965 when the business was sold to A. & D. Fraser (Aberdeen) Ltd., who retained the Morris agency.

Shinnie's were not the only firm dealing with cars in Aberdeen at the beginning of this century. For example, in November 1898, when only three years had passed since cars were allowed unaccompanied on the streets and roads, the Aberdeen Mechanical Society visited Harper's Engineering Works at Craiginches. The visit followed a talk by their President Thomas Mowat, works manager of Harpers, on internal combustion engines. At Harpers they inspected a large Daimler char-a-banc, a De-la-Haye waggonette for 8 persons, a Benz 'sociable', with seats for two on which "members enjoyed a spin through the commodious works", and other cars.

Neither can Shinnie's be given all the credit for coachbuilding in Aberdeen, for there also existed the inventive and highly acclaimed Aberdeen Coach Works of John T. Clark in Rose Street. When the Aberdeen Mechanical Society visited the works in 1896 they had already entered the field of the "horseless carriage". By then, their reputation for elegance of design, lightness of build and fine craftsmanship was well established. John T. Clark was not only carriage builder to Her Majesty the Queen but to many other Royal patrons. He had been admitted to the Worshipful Company of Coach-makers and Coach Harness-makers, London, and made a freeman of the City of London. His works' superintendent was the first to conduct carriage-builders' technical classes in Robert Gordon's College.

In comparatively modest premises with a 50 foot frontage and 230 feet to the rear, Clark employed just over 30 hands in the early 1890s, covering all aspects of carriage making. His specialities read like a catalogue from another world: the Duke of York two-wheeled cart, the Stanhope gig on five springs, Battlesden and village gigs, the Gee Spring Polo, the Glasgow Polo, the Jubilee Car, the duplex reversible waggonette and T cart, the Beatrice Phaeton and many more. His Empress Phaeton was well known in Britain and abroad, as was his Doctor's four-wheel Hansom particularly designed for the medical profession. Two of Clark's inventions had also received attention through their incorporation on his carriages. One was an improved brake; the second a system of levers applied to small carts that could move the body position of the cart relative to the axle when going up or down steep inclines, to improve the balance of the cart. The seats were kept at their proper inclination. Most of Clark's work was for the private market but he also built for the Corporation Fire Brigade the first four-wheel hose reel seen in Aberdeen.

A School Visit

The Middle School in the Gallowgate is not the most handsome of Aberdeen's granite schools but it is a sadder sight than it should be with its windows boarded up (at the time of writing). In 1891 it was a place where the latest techniques in heating, ventilation and education were put into practice by the Aberdeen School Board.

Ventilation was provided by a system of air ducts throughout the school, each classroom being connected by a branch to the main trunk. The air was forced through by a Blackman air propeller, 5 feet in diameter, driven by a 3 horse power gas engine. Seven sets of heating coils conveyed piping hot water from a slow combustion coal furnace to the air intake section where there were about 4000 feet of radiator piping. At this point there was also an air filter of twisted manilla upon which water was sprayed to remove dust and insects. In the days when coal was burnt in profusion, both industrially and socially, such a filter was highly desirable. The effectiveness of the system may be judged by the fact that the air throughout the whole school of 1164 places was changed 8 times an hour at a heating cost of one shilling per day. The temperature maintained in winter was 60 degrees Fahrenheit (15.5 degrees Celsius), cool by today's standards. The system was very similar to that installed at about the same time in the Palace Hotel, as described earlier.

As well as teaching all the usual academic subjects, the school had a gymnasium and a cookery classroom. Technical subjects were by no means commonly taught in schools but a workshop, in which the School Board intended to give manual instruction, included carpenter's benches and tools for 12 boys at a time. The science class room was "a model, its walls being adorned with astronomical and other wall charts".

King Street School, visited the same afternoon, had a similar hot-air ventilation system. As a new school, King Street had been one of the test sites for the forced ventilation system in the early 1880s. One problem was to find the best size and position of the vents in a room to secure both an adequate air flow and satisfactory mixing of the fresh air. At one stage Marischal College Professors were co-opted, Professor Brazier measuring the carbon dioxide levels in class rooms during the teaching day and Professor Niven air flow profiles, speeds and temperatures.

As far as can be judged from their report, the typical classroom had over 100 children and perhaps 2 teachers. Some classes approached 200 and it was quite common for rooms to exceed their capacity calculated at 10 square feet per child. Little wonder that in unventilated rooms pupils suffered lassitude, languor and headaches while open windows created local draughts and brought in disruptive street noise. There was little circulation of the children either, since they *"remained for a considerable portion of the day in the same positions in their seats"*. The background to this less than satisfactory situation was that compulsory education was in its early days. It was not until the Education Act of 1872 (for Scotland) that it was obligatory for all parents to send their children between the ages 5 and 13 to school, and obligatory for the newly elected School Boards to provide the appropriate educational facilities. The implementation of forced ventilation systems in schools was welcomed very favourably by teachers for its improvement in the *"freshness, vigour and health of the pupils"* and for its beneficial effects on staff.

Agricultural Suppliers

The Aberdeenshire landscape of the late nineteenth century was recognisably modern. Admittedly farms were smaller, dykes in better condition and horses provided power in

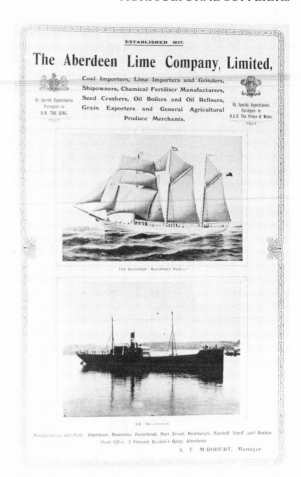

Advertisement for the Aberdeen Lime Co. Ltd., 1907. "Alexander Nicoll" was the last sailing trading ship made in Aberdeen. Courtesy, Aberdeen City Libraries.

the fields and on the dirt roads. It was, however, only in the nineteenth century that great tracts of rural woodland, scrubland and heathland had been converted to workable farmland by stone clearance, drainage, fertilisation and continued use. These improvements had raised Aberdeenshire to the premier cattle breeding county in Britain. The town of Aberdeen benefitted from the expansion of farming by supplying building materials, agricultural implements and general commodities on the one hand, and providing a market centre and export facilities on the other.

The Aberdeen Lime Company were a major supplier of chemical fertiliser, guano, bone-meal, oil-seedcake, lime and coal. Their trade extended to the Orkney and Shetland Isles and they purveyed their products with the Royal Appointment. Established in 1837, they had expanded to cover a two and a half acre site on Provost Blaikie's Quay with production facilities, warehousing and a three-storey granite office block. Beneath their tall chimney, a 96 tube Green's economiser preheated water for a boiler 30 feet long by 8 feet

Letterhead of the Aberdeen Lime Co. Ltd. Courtesy, Aberdeen University Library.

in diameter. Two and a half tons of steam per hour were superheated to achieve the greatest efficiency from their 230 horse power horizontal steam engine that drove all the machinery. Linseed and cotton seed were the primary raw materials for their oil production. The seed was crushed to extract the oil which was subsequently boiled, refined and stored in large raised tanks. Hydraulic presses made seedcake from the residue, with an oil content varying from 12% to 80% depending on the quality of the cake.

The Northern Agricultural Co. Ltd. at Waterloo Quay carried on similar business. When the Aberdeen Mechanical Society visited them in 1902 they watched *"monster stones crushing the seed and preparing it for conversion into cakes"*. Locust beans supplemented linseed and cotton seed. In the early 1930s the Northern Agricultural Co. and Aberdeen Lime amalgamated as Nalco.

Ice Making

Of course it was natural that the harbour area should attract industries using bulky products, such as those imported by the Aberdeen Lime Company. The harbour was also the centre of industry supported by the fishing fleet, which had grown dramatically in prosperity with the advent of the steam trawler. By 1907, some 80,000 tons of fish were landed annually with a value of about one million pounds sterling. To service some 200 steam trawlers and 40 steam liners based at the port and others that called to land fish, required 270,000 tons of coal annually, about half the

Harpers Craiginches Ironworks. A small horizontal steam engine spans the foreground, electric power replaces steam in the rear. Courtesy, North East of Scotalnd Museums Service.

coal brought to the harbour. Four large ice factories *"kept running day and night"* supplied 65,000 tons of ice both in blocks and pre-crushed.

The main purveyors of ice were the North-Eastern Ice Co. Ltd. in Commercial Road (visited in 1892 and 1912), the Aberdeen Ice Manufacturing Co. Ltd. in Poynernook Road (visited in 1896) and the Bon-Accord Ice and Cold Storage Co., also in Poynernook Road, visited in 1904. To make ice requires power to remove energy from the water. In 1892 the North-Eastern Ice Co. used a 30 horse power horizontal engine to drive an ammonia-based refrigeration plant capable of freezing 140 cells of 5 hundredweights each. Their capacity was 280 tons per week *"and is not infrequently taxed to the limit"*. It was indicative of the expansion in the fish trade that twelve years later Bon-Accord Ice could produce 100 tons in 24 hours, and soon after they advertised production at over 1000 tons per week.

Other Industries

In this and previous chapters I have chosen the best-informed accounts of visits by the Aberdeen Mechanical Society. The comparatively few omitted have been mainly those that duplicated industries already described. Not included were the Torry Sawmills of William Fiddes & Sons (visited in 1908), a four acre site comprising a box factory, machinery for making barrels, two saw mills and *"eighty-five machines for the production of the firm's specialities"*; A. Wilson & Sons' Balmoral Granite Works, one of the largest in town covering 2 acres, visited in 1903; the University Press (1898) and the press of Cornwall & Sons (1899). Omitted specifically for lack of contemporary description have been the soap and candle works of Alex. Ogston & Sons (visited in 1897), later to become Ogston & Tennant; the Sandilands Chemical Works of John Miller (visited 1901), noted for its production of sulphuric acid, and James Garvie & Sons Steam Joinery and Cabinet Works, 55 Rose Street (visited 1895).

Curiously enough, scarcely any engineering works were visited. The exceptions were Harpers Craiginches Ironworks, who specialised in all aspects of transmission machinery (visited 1893 and, as mentioned earlier, briefly in 1898) and the 1909 visit to the Ashgrove Engineering Works of Allan Bros., at Kittybrewster, who built oil engines (i.e.

The assembly department of Harpers Craiginches Iron-works, 1907, specialising in power transmission components.

A corner of the turnery at Craiginches Ironworks. Castings were brought directly from the foundry on rails, to be machined here by shafting lathes, key-way slotters, milling machines, shaft key-grooving machines, boring mills and other facilities.

petrol, paraffin or diesel) of 3 to 20 horse power mainly for export. A number of other firms were suggested for visits but we are deprived of tours round William M'Kinnon's & Co. (see chapter 1); Barry, Henry & Co., who specialised in gearing, shafting, pulleys, waterwheels and small steam engines; John M. Henderson & Co., noted for cableways, bridges, retort machinery and much more; James Abernethy & Co., Clyne, Mitchell & Co. Ltd. and, before they were taken over, Blaikie Bros. Footdee Iron Works, all engineers, boilermakers and iron founders; and several smaller firms.

The Caledonian Barley and Meal Mills of John Milne & Co. were larger than either of the mills described in chapter 5. The omission of the comb works of S. R. Stewart & Co. from the visiting programme is surprising, for the works were one of Aberdeen's most famous enterprises in the nineteenth century and into the twentieth century. During the years 1889 to 1895, David Stewart, son of the founder of the comb works and senior partner of the firm, was Aberdeen's Lord Provost and an Honorary President of the Aberdeen Mechanical Society. The Stewart Park was named after him and in 1896 he was knighted. The comb works were proposed for a visit in 1895 and a short description of his impressive business must be included here for completeness. In 1899 the Aberdeen Combworks Co. Ltd. was formed by the amalgamation of S. R. Stewart & Co., the Rosemount Comb Manufacturing Co. Ltd. (whose offices were at 33 Forbes Street) and the York firm of G. Steward & Sons.

The small lathe bay at Craiginches Ironworks. Two miles of overhead rail around the factory carried goods between machines. Most machines were driven by shafting powered by electric motors.

One of the 5 foundry bays at Craiginches Ironworks in 1907 where a total of 100 tons of castings could be produced per week.

Small horizontal steam engine by John M. Henderson, King Street Engineering Works (1888). Courtesy, John M. Henderson & Co. Ltd.

Travelling crane (1888). Courtesy, John M. Henderson & Co. Ltd.

Mobile cable windlass by John M. Henderson (1894). Courtesy, John M. Henderson & Co. Ltd.

Portable steam boiler (1894). Courtesy John M. Henderson & Co. Ltd.

John M. Henderson (1908), who inherited John M. Henderson, King Street Engineering Works from his father and continued to expand the works. Courtesy, Aberdeen City Libraries.

Stages in the production of combs from horn, illustrated by material from Aberdeen Combworks. Courtesy, Aberdeen Art Gallery & Museums, Aberdeen City Arts Department.

The Aberdeen Combworks

The works were begun in Aberdeen in 1830 and long before the end of the century had expanded to become the largest of their kind in the world. On a site of three and a half acres, 1000 hands were employed mainly in a large four-storey building with a frontage of 325 feet on Hutcheon Street. Horn was the commonest raw material and such was the volume of production that over 100,000 horns were imported into the factory each week, contributing to an annual production of 25 million combs per year. Aberdonians were familiar with the somewhat gruesome sight of heaps of horns on the harbour quayside. The solid tips of the horns were re-exported for button making, knife handles, pipe mouthpieces, umbrella handles and other products. Thirty tons a week of sawdust was ground into a fine powder for despatch to agricultural fertiliser manufacturers.

Inside S.R. Stewart & Co.'s Aberdeen combworks. The cut horn was heated on the right before being pressed flat in the vices on the left. Courtesy, ACW Ltd.

The horn was first divided, heated and opened up so that rectangular pieces could be squared, trimmed and pressed flat in a vice. The sweet smell of heated horn was considered pleasant only by those who became accustomed to it. The combs themselves were cut either with small circular saws, for the finest dressing combs with many teeth to the inch, or with an ingenious 'twinning' machine, operated by a man and a boy to the accompaniment of an incessant and peculiar clatter. This machine made two combs out of each piece, the tapering teeth of each comb exactly interleaving each other. Much of the machinery used for the teeth cutting was made by the Company's own engineers to their own valuable patent design.

Inside one of the cutting rooms of the combworks where the rectangular plates of horn were each cut into two combs by the 'twinning' machines around the edge of the room. Courtesy, ACW Ltd.

After being cut out, the combs still had to be pointed, scoured and polished using machine-driven rotary buffs and an enormous amount of labour. The scouring in particular was done with bath-brick and water, which reduced the men and boys in this department to the appearance of brick-makers. By contrast, in the circular sawing room a dense atmosphere of horn dust gave everything and everyone within the white appearance characteristic of a flour miller. Perhaps it was the extensive use of labour that discouraged the Aberdeen Mechanical Society from including the works on their early visiting programme. There was, however, still sufficient machinery in the factory to merit a large 300 horse power engine and three smaller ones besides.

Some horn was chemically treated to create imitation tortoiseshell, but real tortoiseshell, rhinoceros, buffalo and other exotic horns were also used in small quantities for particularly expensive combs. Some ware was carved or elaborately decorated by fret saw, according to the fashion of the times. In all some 2,000 varieties and sizes of comb were produced, from ordinary pocket combs to fancy dressing combs, braid combs, side combs, dog combs and mane combs. Besides combs, a variety of horn goods were made such as paper-knifes, spoons, snuff boxes, drinking cups, shoe horns and bookmarkers.

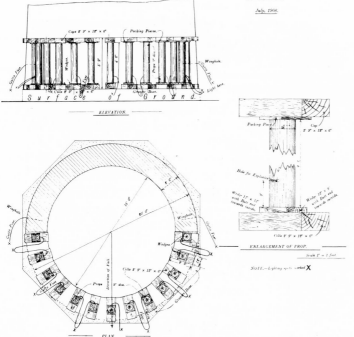

The detonation plan for felling the Bleachfield chimney in 1908. Courtesy, Aberdeen Mechanical Society.

"Aberdeen horn" was, on occasions, the fashionable material for ornamentation.

As a substitute for ivory and other horns, celluloid became popular at the beginning of this century. It was manufactured from camphor and the resulting products were all flammable. Several unpleasant accidents in which ladies' hair combs ignited when adjacent to the cooker or gas light gave publicity to this property of celluloid. The combworks did not follow the trend but introduced their own synthetic material "Keronyx" made from casein, a milk by-product. Since Keronyx, like horn, was not flammable, emphasis was placed on this aspect of the material, but it could also be turned, moulded and highly polished.

Under the name of ACW Ltd. the works still survive, occupying part of the same site and now using modern substitutes for the old natural raw materials. Employing plastic injection moulding, they produce a wide variety of goods.

The Bleachfield Chimney

It is appropriate to end this account of Aberdeen's diverse industries with a visit made by the Aberdeen Mechanical Society that represented the passing of old ways. In July 1908, they were invited to watch the spectacle of Richard's Bleachfield chimney at Rubislaw being demolished.

The stack was a noted landmark in the city. Built in 1846, it stood 242 feet high, 20 feet in diameter at the base, contained over a quarter of a million bricks and was estimated to weigh 1200 tons. The disused chimney had been damaged by lightning in 1906 and begun to deteriorate to such an extent that it had been deemed a hazard to public safety. "*The Aberdeen Journal's*" reporter on the evening of the demolition found himself an hour before the appointed time in streets "*thronged with apparently endless streams of men, women and children all hurrying to be in at the death*". The huge gathering of spectators was estimated at over 30,000. "*Sharply outlined against the dull grey sky, the tall, graceful stalk seemed to carry its years lightly, but, yet, with its life of usefulness over, it was about to get a terrible fall and disappear for ever...*".

Half an hour before the scheduled time, members of the Aberdeen Association of

Civil Engineers and the Aberdeen Mechanical Society inspected the demolition preparations. Part of the base had been knocked out and underpinned by 13 wooden props, all the work being done by hand for fear of initiating a premature collapse. Each prop was to be shattered by 3 ounces of gelignite, timed at one second intervals by the lengths of connecting fuse. The engineers retreated. In breathless silence the spectators waited, all eyes upon the chimney. A dull report, a cloud of smoke, with flying splinters the first prop shattered. Explosion followed explosion, the stalk began to sway. For a few seconds it hung; the base crumbled, the top tilted, the chimney rent asunder in the middle. With a dull grinding noise it crumbled into a mass of debris, the huge crowd cheering. *"A beautiful fall"* was the general verdict. The top had landed within 130 feet of the base. After a few minutes *"thousands of boys and girls were soon swarming over the debris, and in a short time the heap was hidden from view by children"*.

CHAPTER

8

Mechanics at Home and Away

Visits Further Afield

Although the Aberdeen Mechanical Society has always drawn mainly on the town for its membership, it has never been parochial in its outlook. To appreciate Aberdeen's industries in the wider context, from 1893 onwards the Society instituted visits to more distant works. Initially these took place on the Autumn holiday in September but they soon became a regular feature of the May Day holiday.

In 1893 the Society went only as far as the Admiralty Harbour of Refuge works at Peterhead. This immense project was funded by the Treasury as part of a convict employment scheme to undertake building works in the national interest. It provided the reason for siting the prison at Peterhead. The scheme involved constructing 1000 feet of northern breakwater and 3,250 feet of southern breakwater bedded down 40 feet below low water level. The body of the breakwater was made of 50 ton concrete blocks laid in courses, the whole being faced with massive granite ashlar, also in courses. It was for quarrying the 75,000 tons of stone needed annually that the convicts were mainly employed. The engineering aspects were on quite a scale:

giant 50 ton Titan and Goliath cranes (appropriately named) were built and many smaller ones besides; miles of railway line and sidings specially constructed; stone-crushing plant, stone-dressing sheds, engineering and smiths' shops erected for the purpose. The work was begun in 1886, employed a workforce of a few hundred and was scheduled to take about 35 years. In the event it was not finished until 1956.

Ensuing visits by the Society concentrated on the larger engineering and manufacturing works in Scotland, mainly around Glasgow and the neighbouring cities. In 1898, the great Singer works at Kilbowie were visited where 7,000 employees turned out 10,000 sewing machines a week from the lightest dressmaking kind to the heaviest bootmaking machine. 2,000 hands alone were employed in the foundry. The latest automatic machinery showed the way manufacturing was moving. One man could have charge of 7 machines, each with multiple spindles drilling 21 holes simultaneously into the sole-plate of a sewing machine. Taking another example, the sewing machine needle is a precision ground and polished part, with the eye located precisely on the central line. The pro-

Lifting a massive concrete block with a Titan crane in the early stages of building the South Breakwater at Peterhead. Courtesy, North East of Scotland Museums Service.

duction of these needles from coils of wire was done entirely by automatic machinery. This emphasis on efficient production was symbolised by a huge clock 27 feet in diameter mounted in the middle of the works on a 200 foot tower. One wonders what the more enlightened members of the visiting party thought of the social implications of trends seen at Kilbowie.

In 1901 a visit was made to the shipbuilding yard of William Denny Bros. at Dumbarton. It covered ten times the area of Aberdeen's largest yard, employing close on 3,000 hands over a 60 acre site. Seven berths alongside the river Leven could accommodate vessels from 350 feet to 600 feet in length. Among the facilities at Denny's yard was the only model-testing tank in Britain outside the Admiralty's at Torquay. It was 300 feet long and 10 feet deep, built to the design of William Froude F.R.S. who is still well known for the fundamental work he did on establishing the validity of using scale models to predict the performance of full-sized vessels. During their visit, the Society saw being constructed the first passenger turbine boat in the world, the 'King Edward'. These and other innovations demonstrated that the Scottish shipbuilding industry had every reason to be proud of its achievements.

Many visits showed Society members the inside of other works whose names were familiar to every member. Redpath Brown & Co., at Edinburgh (visited 1899) were known for their large girder works, boilers and hydraulic tools; D. Bruce Peebles & Co., Bonnington (1902) for their electric motors and dynamos; Mirrlees, Watson & Co. Ltd., Glasgow (1910) as pioneers in this country of diesel engine manufacture; Babcock & Wilcox Ltd., Renfrew (1905) for their multi-tubular boilers. This last firm employed 2,000 men on a 32 acre site entirely devoted to making boilers. Taken along with their American plant, their output was the largest in the world at 10 boilers a day. The Hyde Park Locomotive Works of the North British Locomotive Co. in Glasgow employing 3,500 hands on a 16 acre site showed, quite naturally, a larger scale of locomotive building than that needed for the comparatively small GNSR at Inverurie. Among other work in 1903 "the firm have at present in course of construction thirty-two locomotives for the Canadian Pacific Railway, which are the largest and most powerful yet built in this country, and immense-looking structures they are when seen complete with large tenders and cowcatchers".

Looking at Aberdeen around the year 1900 from the perspective of 'big industry' in other parts of the country, it is clear that Aberdeen was at the top of the table in the granite trade, the fishing industry and in the speciality of comb making. In paper making and shipbuilding it was well placed (only one of Aberdeen's three largest yards have been covered in this book); in textiles and other industries it had significant presence. Perhaps most importantly, it had a diversity of industry that serviced a wide range of local needs. Moreover, virtually all its industries were founded by local men and they ploughed back their profits into the local economy. A significant amount of machinery was still designed locally and built locally. The workforce taken as a whole were owners, directors, managers, administrators, clerks and labourers; the same was generally true of the service industries. What comes across strongly is the sense of civic enterprise, identity, cohesion and pride that was present in Aberdeen at the beginning of the century. This is not a view generated by councillors, politicians or the press but is obtained by simply observing achievements in the city. It is of course an oversimplification, but will our descendants judge equally favourably on our own civic achievements and what we have done with our inheritance?

Lecture Topics for Winter Evenings

In comparison with the visits, the regular winter season meetings of the Aberdeen Mechanical Society in Robert Gordon's mechanical class-room were more specialised and less well attended. Twenty seems to have been a reasonable audience in the early years, though numbers increased to several times this by the beginning of the twentieth century.

Steam still ruled on land and sea. Typical talks were "The Management of Marine Boilers", "Economical Production of Steam Power", "Improvements in Boiler Making", "Steam Engine Economy", "Mechanical Stokers", "Steam Turbines" and so on. Locomotives occupied as much attention as marine engineering with talks such as "The Modern Locomotive", "The Compound Locomotive", "Locomotive Boilers" and "Railway Brakes", advocating the efficiency of automatic vacuum brakes, bearing witness to the strong presence of GNSR personnel in the Society.

Why was the steam engine such a central mechanism in the nineteenth century? It appeared ubiquitously in factories, on the railways, on building sites and at sea. The answer is found if one thinks merely of the unskilled component of the effort required to perform many jobs: jobs such as lifting earth from a trench or turning a shaft to drive a machine. One could ask how much effort was required by a machine compared with the effort required by manpower? A rough answer is obtained quite simply from the laws that govern machinery. Using nineteenth century technology, five tons of coal and a steam engine could perform as much effort as a working man over his entire life. That one fact alone showed the industrial value of fuel and steam engines compared with muscle power.

Accidents involving machinery have always formed a dark cloud over the engineering scene. In a talk given by John Calder, H.M. Inspector of Factories, on *The Prevention of Accidents in Factories*" in 1899, a statistic was quoted that 3,700 persons were killed in British Industry and 71,000 injured in the previous year. Talks during the previous decade on "*Some Land Boiler Defects*", "*Accidents to Machinery at Sea*", "*Defects of Propeller Shafts*", "*Railway Safety Appliances*" and "*Automatic Arrangements for Extinguishing Fires*" had focused members attention on the need for safety design.

Although it seemed regular practice to throw drive belts onto rapidly rotating shafting, there was at least some awareness that a combination of care and appropriate design could save accidents. By today's standards, there was negligible awareness of industrial

Boiler explosions were a worrying hazard of the steam age.

health hazards. One contemporary writer visiting a railway workshop commented "*until you have heard a dozen or more mechanical air-driven riveters and caulkers at work on a boiler shell simultaneously you don't know what real noise is. Though I put my hand to my mouth and bellowed into my guide's ear, I quite failed to keep in communication with him; and my throat growing sore with the exercise, I soon abandoned all attempts at conversation*". It is only comparatively recently that prolonged use of vibrating tools has been known to cause permanent damage to circulation in the hands and forearms. In addition to noise and vibration, the granite industry offered the hazards of dust and flying granite chips. One cannot help conclude that Aberdonians have paid for their fine granite city not only through their forefathers' wages but also through their health. Since later generations have not had to win the stone, it has become easy to undervalue it.

If there was a theme towards the end of the nineteenth century, it was the growing importance of electricity. By 1889 the versatility of the industrial electric motor was being felt, with members being introduced to electric conveyor belts, electric lifts and electric tramways. The newly invented electric drill for making rivet holes in ships' plates was not welcomed at first, on account of the level of expertise required. Electric lighting was on everyone's minds in the early 1890s, partly because the Edison-Swan patent expired in 1893. After the expiry, the cost of electric lamps was expected to plummet. Even with the efficiency attainable in 1893, to produce illumination it was much better to use gas to drive an engine that turned a dynamo that ran an electric light, than to burn the gas directly in a lamp. The advent of the Welsbach incandescent gas-mantle soon afterwards shifted the balance back towards the direct use of gas, with the result that gas lighting in houses and offices, and on the streets, was given a new lease of life even when electricity was available. Electricians, of course, fought this reverse to their fortunes by successfully improving the electric lamp, developing the new, bright, metal filament bulbs early in the twentieth century.

One active founder member who promoted electrical interest in the Society was the appropriately named A. Spark. Alex Spark was a scientific instrument maker in the

Beautiful engraving on the boiler insurance policy covering Thomas Tait's papermill for 1891 reminds clients of the consequences of an accident. Courtesy, Tait Paper.

Town and at times a committee member of the Society. Some of his instruments bought by Robert Gordon's College and by the Natural Philosophy Department of the University can still be seen amongst the historical collections in these two institutions.

It was A. Spark who gave the first talk on *"Electric Lighting"* in 1890, followed later in the month by Professor Niven on *"The Electric Discharge in Air and in Rarified Gases"*, the phenomenon that underlies the modern fluorescent tube but which was then a long way from commercial exploitation. Later talks on *"Dynamos"*, *"Power Transmission"*, *"Small Electric Plant"* and *"The Public Electricity Supply"* reflected the expanding interest in these fields. A talk on *"Electric Railways and Tramways"* by the famous Professor Andrew Jamieson of the Glasgow and West of Scotland Technical College, was well timed in 1898 to coincide with Aberdeen's planning of the electrification of its own tramway system. Lord Provost Fleming and Councillors joined in a lively discussion at the end on how Aberdeen could avoid the unsightliness of lines of iron poles supporting the overhead wires, such as had appeared in Glasgow. Councillor Boddie seemed fairly horrified by the whole prospect, exclaiming *"We'll never have our principal streets covered with wire*

'riddles' like that, as in Glasgow". Although the Councillor raised the unappealing spectacle of daylight reaching the darkened streets below in patches through a sieve of overhead wires, it never became that bad. Once the public had experienced the initial electrification, they were in fact impatient for its completion and the spread of the system.

Professor Jamieson was invited as part of a deliberate Society policy to include at least one visiting speaker per year from outwith the City. In 1903 John Gray of London, nephew of the founder of the School of Art, gave a well-informed lecture to an audience of no less than 700 on *"Radium and Radio Activity"*, showing radium itself only a year after its time-consuming isolation by Marie Curie. He covered all the speculations of the day: that radioactivity necessitated a revision of the accepted ideas of atomic theory; that it was ultimately the source of the earth's heat and therefore implied a complete revision of the estimated age of the earth; that it could be responsible for the sun's heat; that it could be a source of power; that it could kill bacterial colonies and cure some cancers. Almost every one of these speculations has proved correct, but usually in more complicated ways than those seen at the time. Nuclear engineering was still several decades away as a profession.

Taking just two more examples, in 1904 Dr A. Ogg gave *"a very learned but clearly presented"* talk on *"The Microscopic Structure of Carbon Steels"*. Dr Ogg was an Aberdeenshire man and one of the first B.Sc. and Ph.D. students of Aberdeen University, having studied under Professor Niven. He subsequently took the high road of scientific research with a scholarship to Germany but, by 1904, had returned to Britain to the Royal Naval Engineering College at Devonport. In 1911, Dr. P. D. Innes of Heriot Watt College gave a remarkable demonstration of *"Wireless Telephony"*, eleven years before the BBC was founded and 12 years before Aberdeen's *"2 BD"* began calling from Belmont Street. There was, of course, a continuing interest in lectures on more practical topics of immediate utility.

Because of the wide-ranging interests of members, the Society was very much aware of kindred societies in Aberdeen. As well as the Aberdeen Association of Civil Engineers (founded 1900), there were the Aberdeen Photographic Society (founded 1889), The Society of Practical Model Engineers (absorbed into the Mechanical Society in 1903), the Scientific Society, the Mathematical Society, the Working Men's Natural History and Antiquarian Society, the Aberdeen Model Steamer Club, the Aberdeen Society of Architects, and others. The older Aberdeen Philosophical Society had talks from time to time on technical subjects of current interest and R. Gordon Nicol was among Mechanical Society members who belonged to both Societies. There were continuing but informal links with the mechanics' Dundee counterpart, The Dundee Institute of Engineers founded in 1884, which incorporated The Society of Experimental Engineers in 1909. The Mechanical Society were confident of their status, for R. Gordon Nicol could say in 1906 *"A Society such as this has done an enormous amount of good, not only in Aberdeen, but throughout the world, for many of the members of the Aberdeen Mechanical Society have initiated societies of a similar nature in different parts of the world"*.

Initiatives in Education

The provision of technical education in Aberdeen was a recurring theme of the Aberdeen Mechanical Society throughout the 25 years of this survey. Professor Pirie, who was on the Council of the Aberdeen Philosophical Society and who taught mathematics at the University, set one hare running in 1891 when he addressed the Mechanical Society under the title *"Is a Mechanical Department needed in the University?"*. The major extension to the Marischal College building that now dominates its architecture was in its early planning stage. Pirie, acknowledging that he did not have much support within the University, wished to sow the idea among the community of engineers at work in Aberdeen. The proposal was far from novel, for Glasgow, Edinburgh and University College, Dundee, already had professors of Engineering. Moreover, our competitors abroad, particularly in Germany, were well ahead in this field.

To Pirie's disappointment the Society did not take up the idea as strongly as he surely hoped. The members almost all had their feet firmly planted on the workshop floor: they certainly wanted technical education but thought that it should be coupled with more practical training than a University provided. They were right in thinking that practical classes in any non-medical subject in the University were then in their infancy. Andrew Sproul in his presidential address on *"Technical Education"* caught the spirit of their attitude in remarks aimed at existing technical colleges: *"from the Principal downwards, each and all of the staff of technical institutions were sometimes not worth 15/- a week in any establishment where real practical work had to be done. Good technical education must be supplemented by workshop practice..."*. However, by the following decade attitudes had changed and, led by Provost John Fleming in 1900, there was a frequently recurring call for the University to found a Chair of Engineering.

Unfortunately, the simple fact was that the University could not afford such a chair. If it had not been for the generous benefaction of the Aberdonian Tyneside shipbuilding magnate Charles Mitchell and his son, the University would not even have got the building extension it did. In 1902, the Rt. Hon. James Bryce, Liberal M.P. for South Aberdeen, speaking as a member to the Aberdeen Mechanical Society commented *"he hoped that the University would have a well-equipped engineering department in every way, with laboratories and apparatus, and he hoped it would be done by means of a benefaction by Mr Andrew Carnegie"*. On this occasion, Andrew Carnegie did not oblige.

The value of Engineering in a university was emphasised from time to time by extending invitations to the established Scottish Professors of Engineering to speak in Aberdeen. Glasgow had a chair founded in 1840 by Queen Victoria; Edinburgh, a chair instituted in 1868 and University College, Dundee, which was not an autonomous degree-awarding body, a chair in 1882. In a flurry of activity in 1907, T. Hudson Beare from Edinburgh gave a talk in February to close on 300 in Gordon's College gymnasium; in April, Professor Archibald Barr of Glasgow addressed a similar number; in the summer, the Society visited Professor T. Claxton Fiddler on his home ground in University College, Dundee; in November, Aberdeen University's Principal, the Very Rev. J. Marshall Lang addressed the Aberdeen Mechanical Society on *"Education and Educational Values"*.

Though Principal Lang was a classical scholar, he fully supported the Mechanics' desire for improved educational facilities. *"What I observe"*, he said, *"is that towards the making of a thoroughly intelligent workman in any particular branch of industry, a comprehensive scientific knowledge is the desideratum.... The man of the future, be he farm labourer, mechanic, artisan, is not to be a fellow whose luck is up or down with a shilling in his pocket; he is to be a man of knowledge both theoretical and experimental, who understands the laws of successful operation, and so moves on.... but I do not overlook the still wider sweeps of view. The first worth of a man or woman is, the manhood, the womanhood itself. He or she is something more than a 'hand'. More than all crafts and craftsmanship is the humanity"*. He developed the latter point. *"But what I protest against is the tendency to urge the value of education as being a means of getting on, as it is called; to place that always in front, and thereby encourage the feeling that educational success is to be measured by the quality of cloth on the back, or the prefix to a name, or the depth of a purse."* At some length he expanded on the benefits of education, culminating with the summary *"the fullest value of knowledge is its power of making life ... interesting; giving it zest, realising in it an emancipation from the tyranny of circumstance and from things debasing and deteriorative, imparting a real, unfading splendour to the prospects of the*

Principal J. Marshall Lang of Aberdeen University, depicted in 1907, the year he addressed the Aberdeen Mechanical Society. Courtesy, Aberdeen City libraries.

soul, and supplying a meat of which the mind eats and the world knows not. This is in effect, more or less, a truly liberal education – that which is within reach of all".

The debate on the value of education which haunts Aberdeen University in particular at the end of the twentieth-century was clearly in full voice at the beginning of the century. Lang emphasised the dual rôle of University education, manifest by its technical and its humanitarian values; the one largely measurable, the other not. The

Mechanics were well aware of the former, and echoed the prevalent sentiments on the latter by loud applause. What lessons have we learnt during the century? I write this at the end of a decade in which about one half of the academic staff of Aberdeen University have been encouraged to leave and important departments closed. These moves were forced not by any educational failures but by simplistic central Government accounting practices that patently failed to measure the value of the University to the citizens of Aberdeen and its surrounding region. Those who close institutions in response to the political fashions of the day often forget how hard our forefathers fought to establish them. To take only one example, it took thirty years from Pirie's first moves, and a great deal of rhetoric and politics from local business, Councillors, Members of Parliament, Provosts and Principals before the Jackson Chair of Engineering was finally established at Aberdeen in 1922.

On a level more immediate to the needs of the Aberdeen Mechanical Society, they were clearly envious of the facilities formerly enjoyed by the Aberdeen Mechanics Institution. Much needed in Aberdeen was a lecture hall, library and study rooms that could be shared by the Society, the Civil Engineers and the Architects to provide a base for all three organisations. A scheme to pool their resources was promoted for several years by R. Gordon Nicol and others but failed, presumably on account of its cost. More successful was a continual lobbying for a Technical College in Aberdeen.

Since the absorption of the Aberdeen Mechanics Institution by Robert Gordon's College in 1882 - 1884, that body had provided in combination with Gray's School of Art *"Commercial, Scientific, and Technical Instruction for clerks, engineers, surveyors, architects, builders, stonecutters, wood-carvers, painters and decorators, lithographers and engravers, plumbers, chemists, etc."*. By the beginning of this century some 1500 lads annually attended the more advanced evening classes offered by the College. There were in Aberdeen some 600 apprentice mechanical engineers, most of whom would obtain permanent jobs out of Aberdeen, in the world at large. R. Gordon Nicol was moved to comment in 1907 *"Aberdeen did not claim to be an engineering city, but there was one thing which it was in no small measure: it was a nursery for engineers"*. Robert Gordon's College

was doing the best it could but it had neither the equipment, the laboratories nor the staff to provide the kind of Technical College facilities that had become established in Glasgow, Edinburgh, Dundee and other major engineering centres.

The Mechanics and the Civil Engineers promoted the idea of a Technical College assiduously in the first years of this century. By 1908, Provost Sir Alexander Lyon remarked that *"the Technical College was the most important matter before them in Aberdeen at the present moment"*. In 1909, Robert Gordon's Technical College was established under a Provisional Order confirmed by Act of Parliament. The new institution officially came into being on 1st January 1910, with an extensive Board of Governors elected by the Town Council, the University, the Incorporated Trades, the County Council, the Harbour Commissioners and several other bodies. R. Gordon Nicol was co-opted to the Board and among the Committee members overseeing Engineering provision were J. Alex Bell and William J. Pickersgill.

The Technical College was recognised as one of the Central Institutions of Scotland and its Department of Engineering was to be developed under the newly appointed A. R. Horne to include day classes up to University Degree standard. As we look back on the first 25 years of the Aberdeen Mechanical Society, we find that its association with Robert Gordon's College was as strong at the end of this period as at the beginning. Dr John Buchanan, who had been for 26 years a science teacher at the College, was President of the Society in 1911 - 1912. In its 25th year, 1912 - 1913, Alex R. Horne took over the Presidency. R. Gordon Nicol, always close to the pulse of things, commented in that year *"it was not the prominent citizens of Aberdeen who proposed the Technical College. It was the Mechanical Society and the Civil Engineering Society that did so ..... pegging away to get the College established"*. Alex R. Horne later became Professor at Heriot Watt College in Edinburgh.

Finale

The Aberdeen Mechanical Society was founded as a social and educational organisation to bring together mechanical engineers from Aberdeen's wide-ranging industries. Looking over its first 25 years, it unquestionably fulfilled a need, as 200 members by 1900 and over 300 three years later would surely have concurred. The membership and active participation of Provosts, Councillors and senior men from Aberdeen's major industries and services raised the social status of engineers enormously in the city. The annual reunion dinner, instituted in the sixth year of the Society to take place on the Saturday nearest James Watt's birthday, 19th January, regularly received column feet of press coverage in both the *"Aberdeen Daily Journal"* and the *"Aberdeen Free Press"*. One sign of the strength of the Society was that its Council was not dominated by a caucus of enthusiasts but attracted the voluntary help required from engineers in many fields.

When the Society was inaugurated, the *'bogey'* of foreign competition was clearly visible, in the shape of American and German machinery. Far from receding, this spectre grew during the 25 years until engineers felt that they could almost hear the forges in action across the waters of the German Ocean (the North Sea). They certainly saw the advanced American press used to print *"The People's Friend"*, the American machinery that made their boots in local factories and the American electric lift that took them between floors in the Palace Hotel. American

technology was responsible for the Linotype machines that composed their daily papers, the typewriters on the office desk and the Singer sewing machines used in their homes. It was not the cheapness of foreign goods that worried Aberdeen's mechanics as much as the inventiveness of foreign industry. To counter this they saw that the raising of educational standards in Aberdeen was, in the long term, necessary for survival. We have seen how they had some success. They were also successful without any conscious effort in bringing together staff with a common interest in the University and in Robert Gordon's College.

The growth and prosperity of Aberdeen during the 25 years covered by this account was in no way steady, for there were periods of depression and stagnation. Nonetheless, the Aberdeen Mechanical Society continued to attract the attention of engineers, and upon the Society's early strengths they have now built a century of activity. By inclination the Aberdeen Mechanical Society is a forward looking body, but I hope its membership will grant that the centenary year is an appropriate time to write about its first twenty five years and the engineering achievements in the City at large during that time.

INDEX